11+
Non-verbal Reasoning

WORKBOOK 5

Additional Practice Questions

Dr Stephen C Curran

with Andrea Richardson

Edited by Katrina MacKay

This book belongs to

ae PUBLICATIONS

Accelerated Education Publications Ltd

Contents

Chapter Twenty
SIMILARITIES
1. Level One

On the left of each of the rows below there are two figures that are alike. On the right there are five more figures. Find which one of these five is **most like** the two figures on the left.

Example

 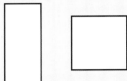

                                 (a)   b   c   d   e

Answer: **a** as the shape has four sides.

Exercise 20: 1   Which figure is most like the two figures on the left?

1)

                                 a   **b**   **c**   **d**   **e**

2)

                                 a   **b**   **c**   **d**   **e**

3)

                                 a   **b**   **c**   **d**   **e**

4)

                                 a   **b**   **c**   **d**   **e**

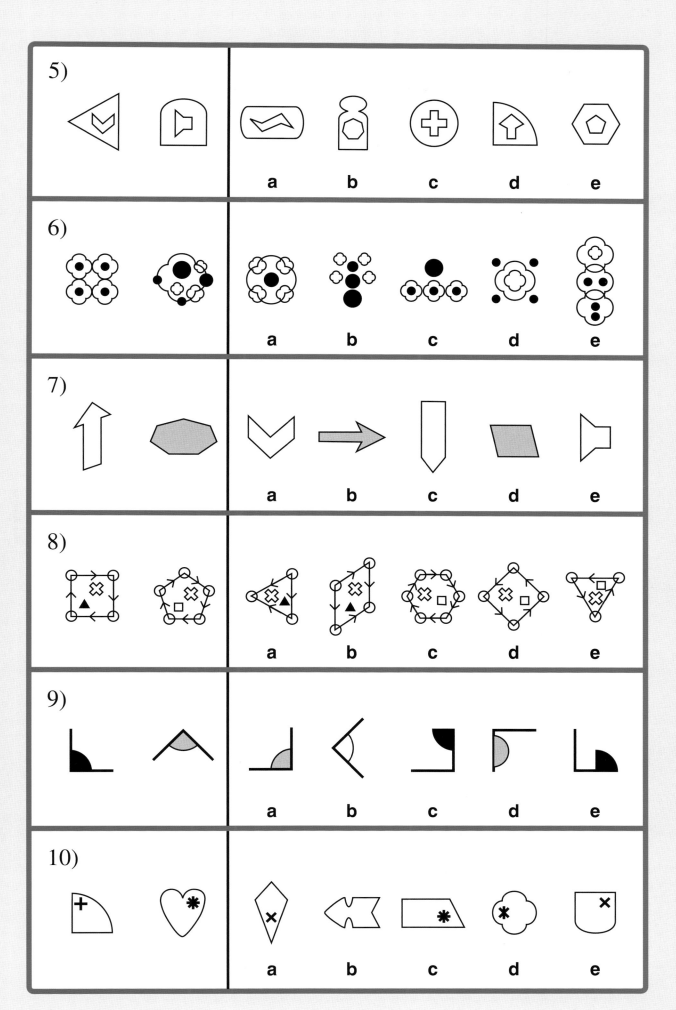

5)

        a   b   c   d   e

6)

        a   b   c   d   e

7)

        a   b   c   d   e

8)

        a   b   c   d   e

9)

        a   b   c   d   e

10)

        a   b   c   d   e

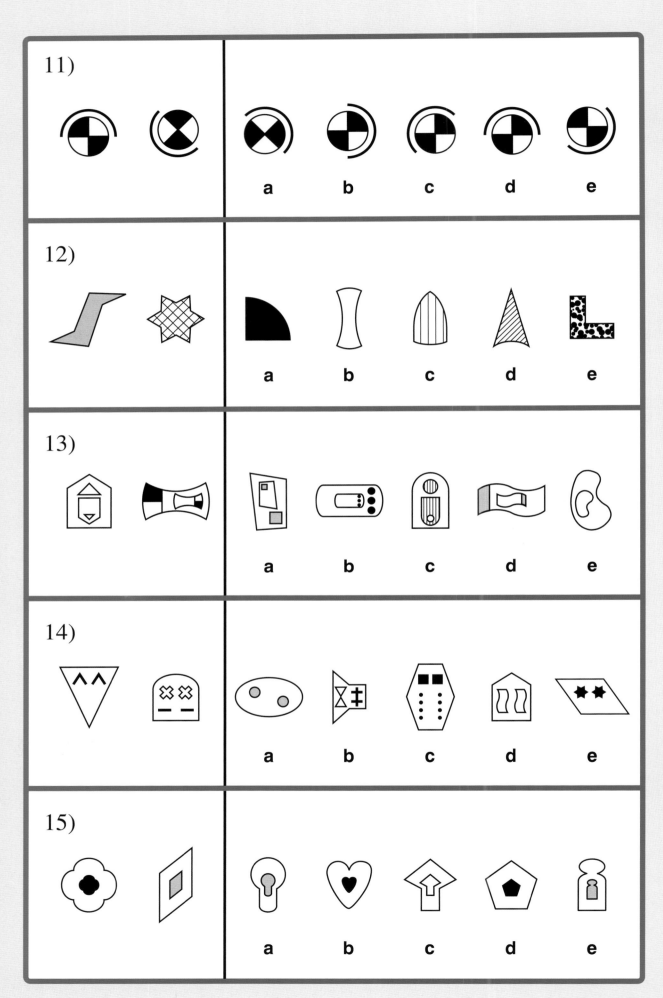

11)

              a   b   c   d   e

12)

               a   b   c   d   e

13)

               a   b   c   d   e

14)

               a   b   c   d   e

15)

               a   b   c   d   e

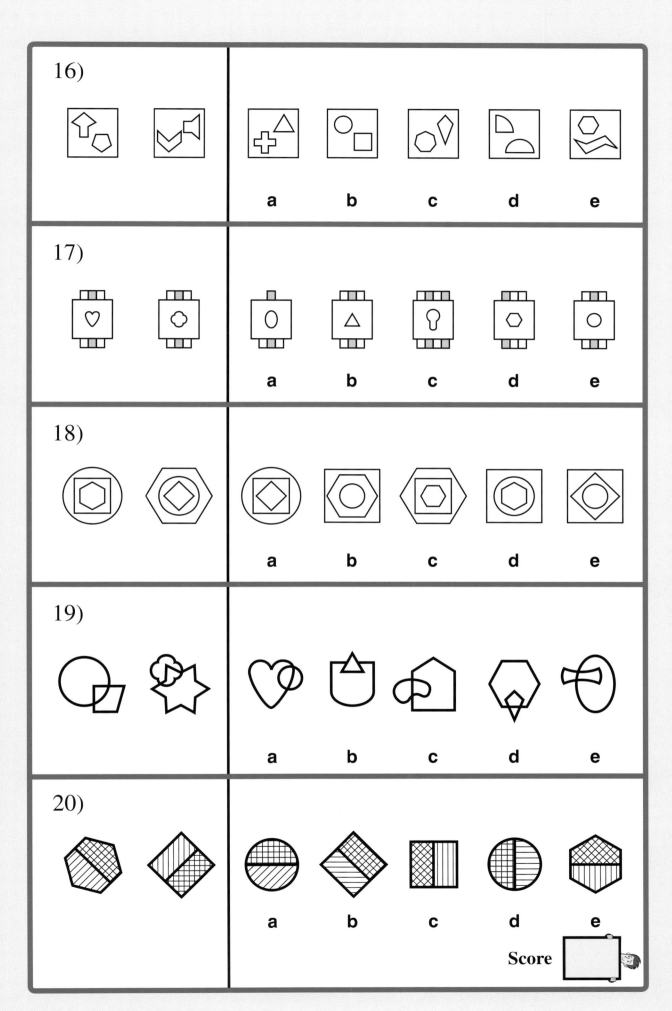

16)

    a   **b**   **c**   **d**   **e**

17)

    a   **b**   **c**   **d**   **e**

18)

    a   **b**   **c**   **d**   **e**

19)

    a   **b**   **c**   **d**   **e**

20)

    a   **b**   **c**   **d**   **e**

Score

7

2. Level Two

On the left of each of the rows below there are two figures that are alike. On the right there are five more figures. Find which one of these five is **most like** the two figures on the left.

Example

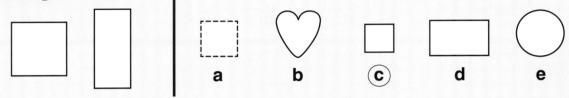

Answer: **c** as the shape has four sides and has a Thin Solid Line.

Exercise 20: 2 Which figure is most like the two figures on the left?

1)

                                  a   **b**   **c**   **d**   **e**

2)

                                  a   **b**   **c**   **d**   **e**

3)

                                  a   **b**   **c**   **d**   **e**

4)

                                  a   **b**   **c**   **d**   **e**

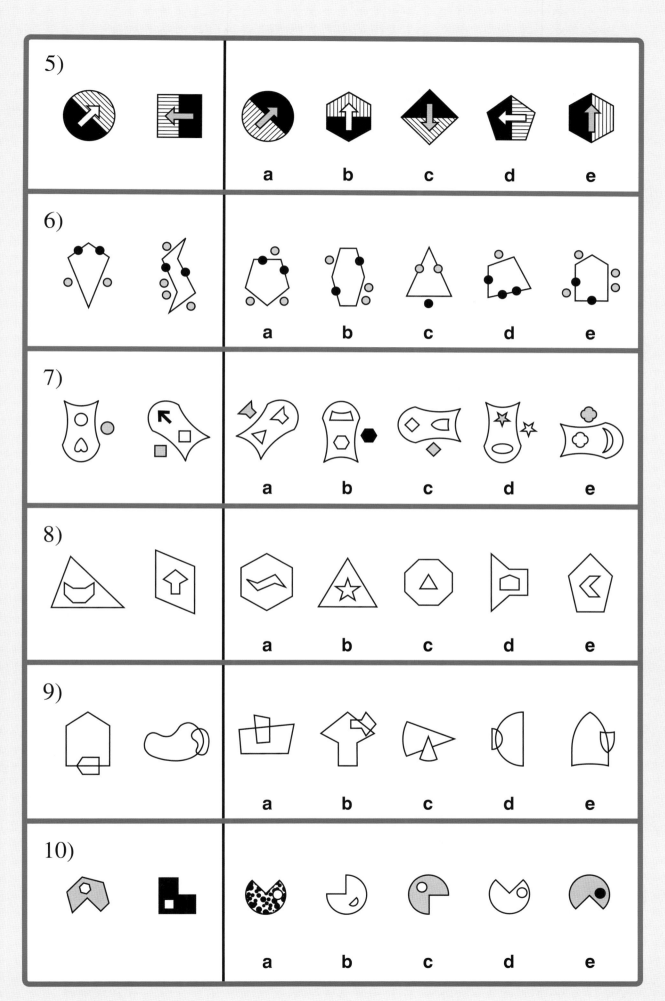

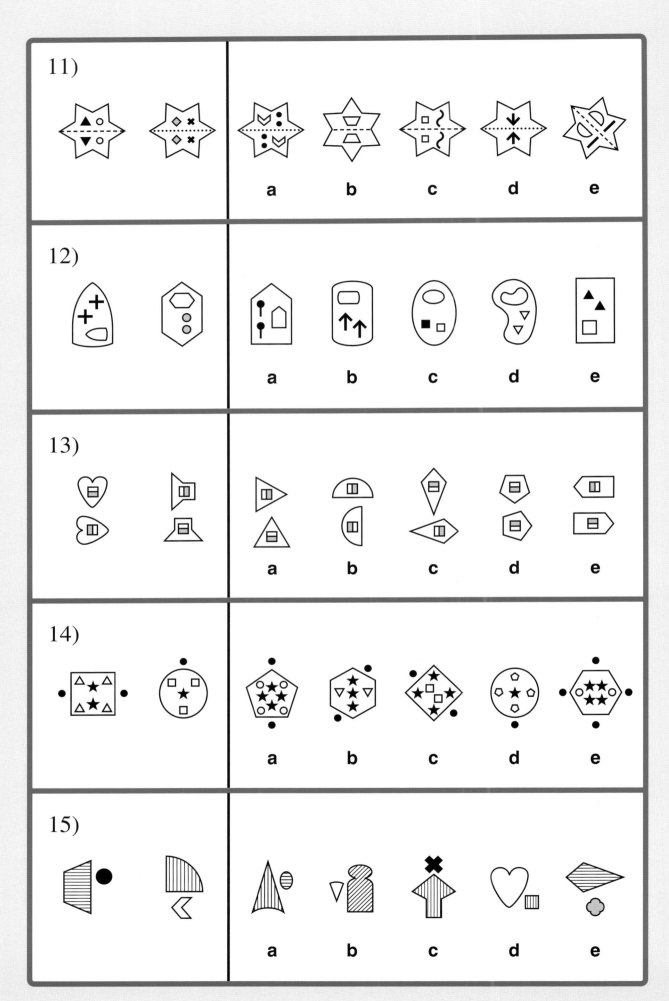

11)

      a   b   c   d   e

12)

      a   b   c   d   e

13)

      a   b   c   d   e

14)

      a   b   c   d   e

15)

      a   b   c   d   e

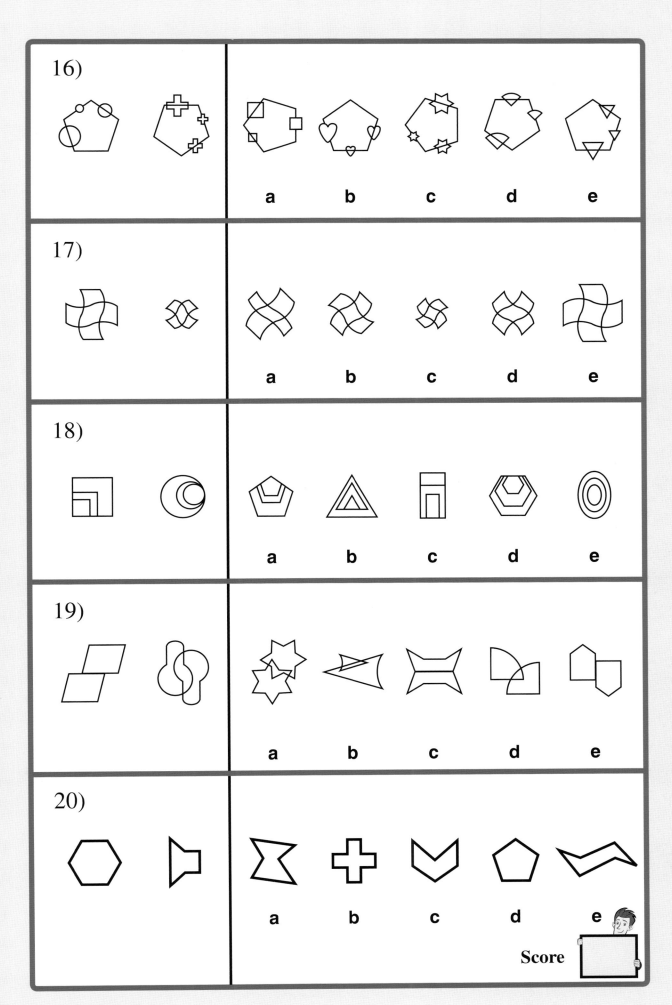

16)   a   b   c   d   e

17)   a   b   c   d   e

18)   a   b   c   d   e

19)   a   b   c   d   e

20)   a   b   c   d   e

Score

3. Level Three

On the left of each of the rows below there are two figures that are alike. On the right there are five more figures. Find which one of these five is **most like** the two figures on the left.

Example

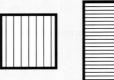   

                         a   **b**   **c**   **ⓓ**   **e**

Answer: **d** as the shape has four sides, has a Thick Solid Line and has a Vertical or Horizontal Shaded Fill.

Exercise 20: 3 Which figure is most like the two figures on the left?

1)

                         a   **b**   **c**   **d**   **e**

2)

                         a   **b**   **c**   **d**   **e**

3)    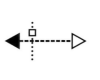

                         a   **b**   **c**   **d**   **e**

4)

                         a   **b**   **c**   **d**   **e**

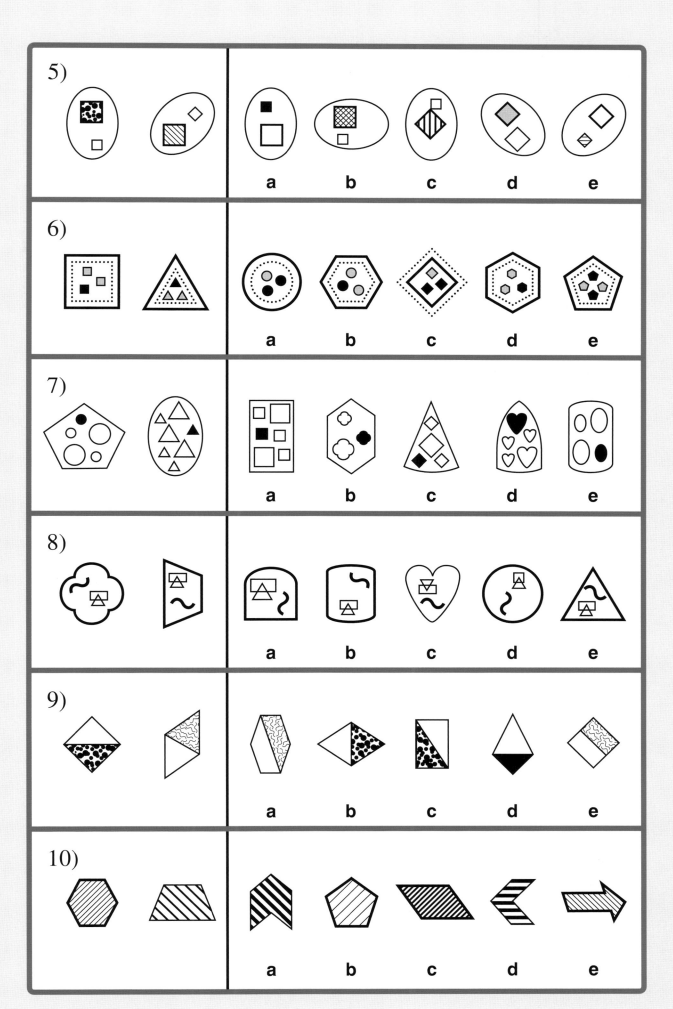

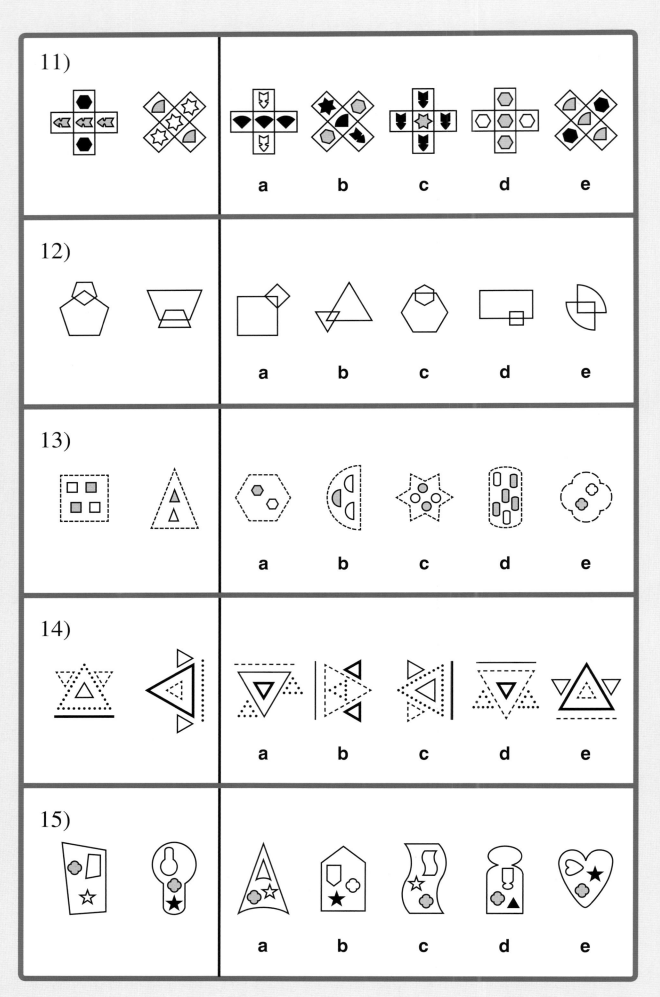

11)

    a   b   c   d   e

12)

    a   b   c   d   e

13)

    a   b   c   d   e

14)

    a   b   c   d   e

15)

    a   b   c   d   e

14

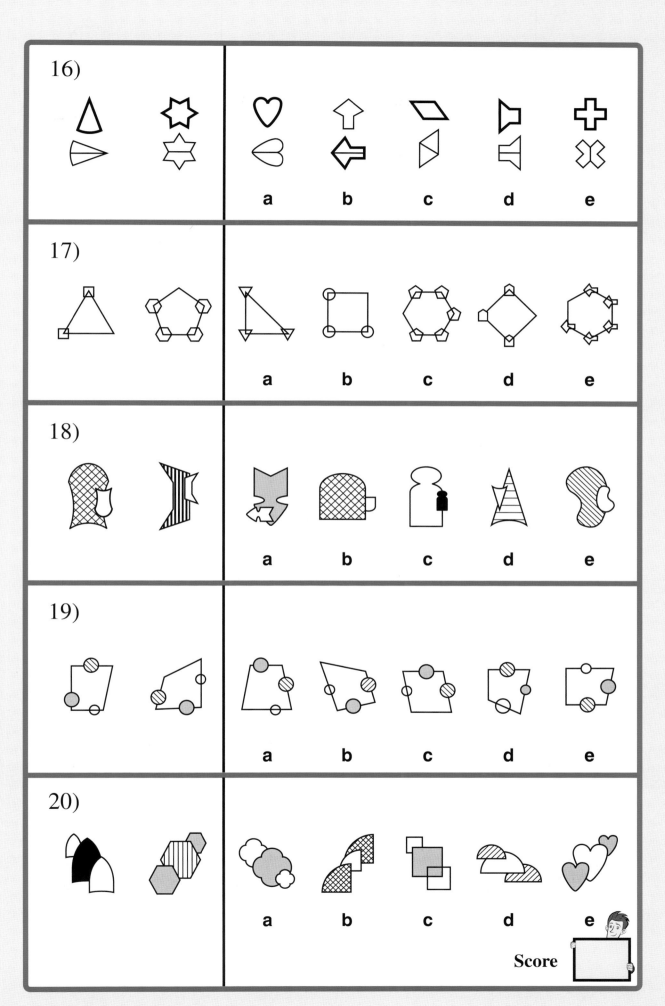

16)

    a   b   c   d   e

17)

    a   b   c   d   e

18)

    a   b   c   d   e

19)

    a   b   c   d   e

20)

    a   b   c   d   e

Score

4. Levels Four & Five

On the left of each of the rows below there are two figures that are alike. On the right there are five more figures. Find which one of these five is **most like** the two figures on the left.

Example

a   b   c   d   (e)

Answer: **e** as the outer shape has four sides, has a Thick Solid Line, has a Vertical or Horizontal Shaded Fill and the same shape with a Black Fill is enclosed within it.

Exercise 20: 4 Which figure is most like the two figures on the left?

1)

                       a   b   c   d   e

2)

                       a   b   c   d   e

3)

                       a   b   c   d   e

4)

                       a   b   c   d   e

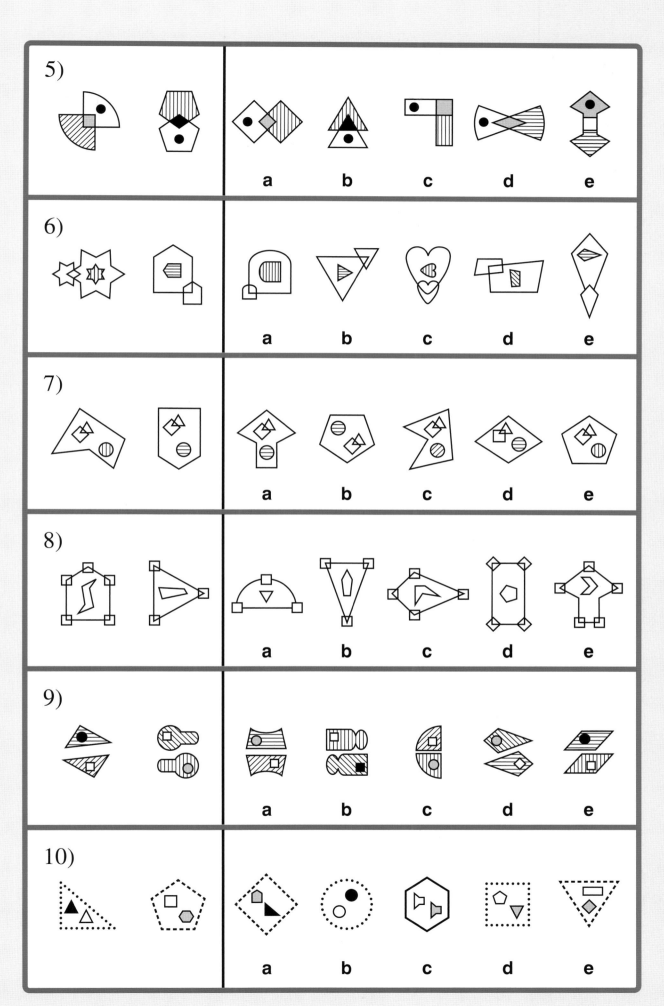

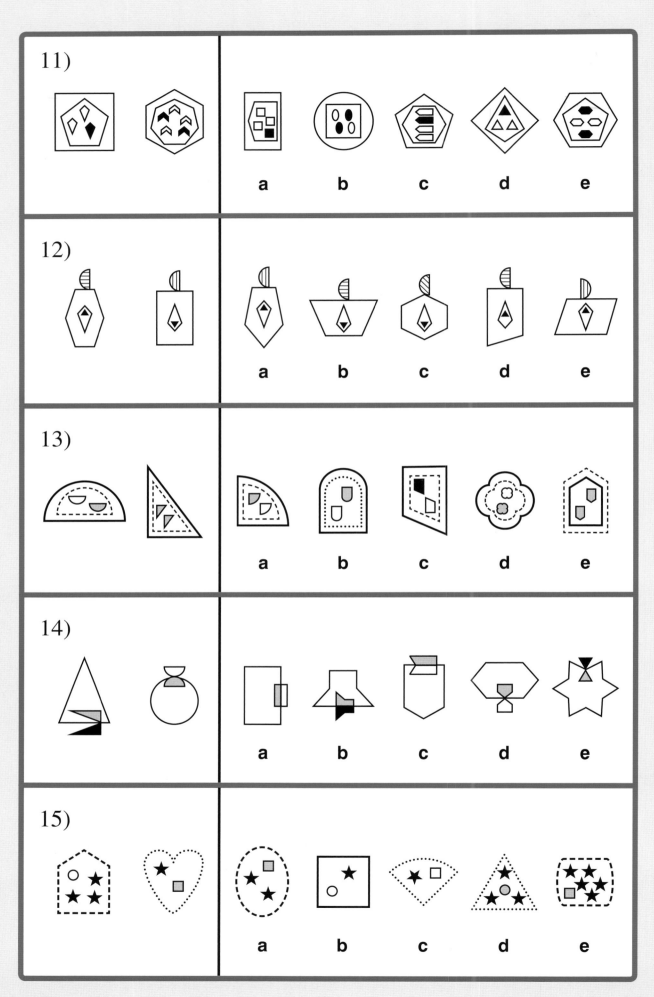

11)

      a   b   c   d   e

12)

      a   b   c   d   e

13)

      a   b   c   d   e

14)

      a   b   c   d   e

15)

      a   b   c   d   e

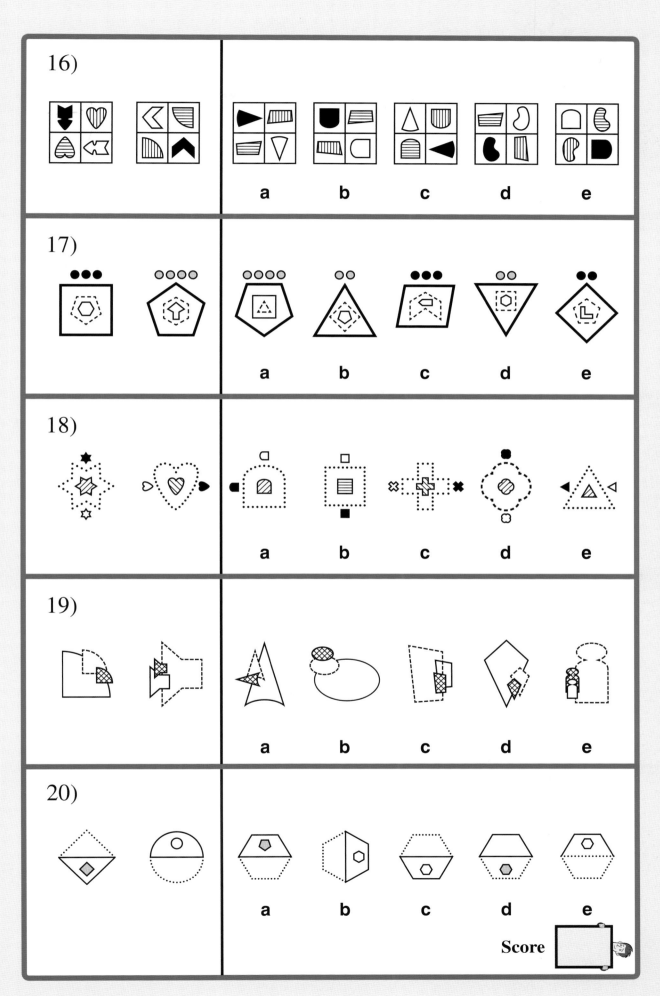

16)

a b c d e

17)

a b c d e

18)

a b c d e

19)

a b c d e

20)

a b c d e

Score

5. Mixed Levels

Exercise 20: 5 Which figure is most like the two figures on the left?

1)
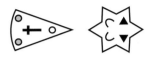

         a   **b**   **c**   **d**   **e**

2)
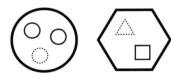

         a   **b**   **c**   **d**   **e**

3)

         a   **b**   **c**   **d**   **e**

4)

         a   **b**   **c**   **d**   **e**

5)

         a   **b**   **c**   **d**   **e**

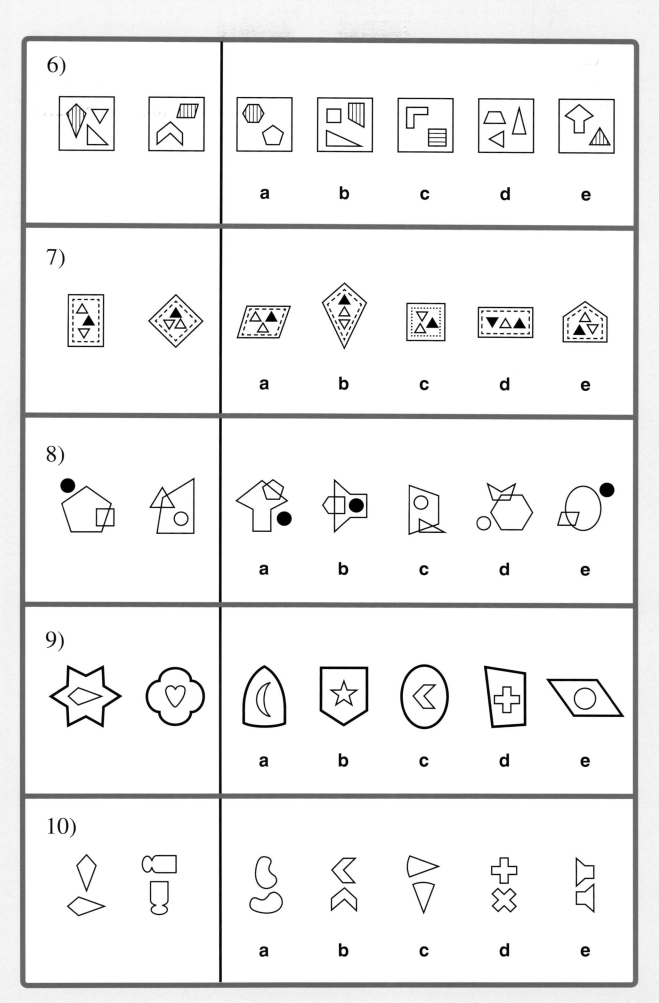

© 2011 Stephen Curran

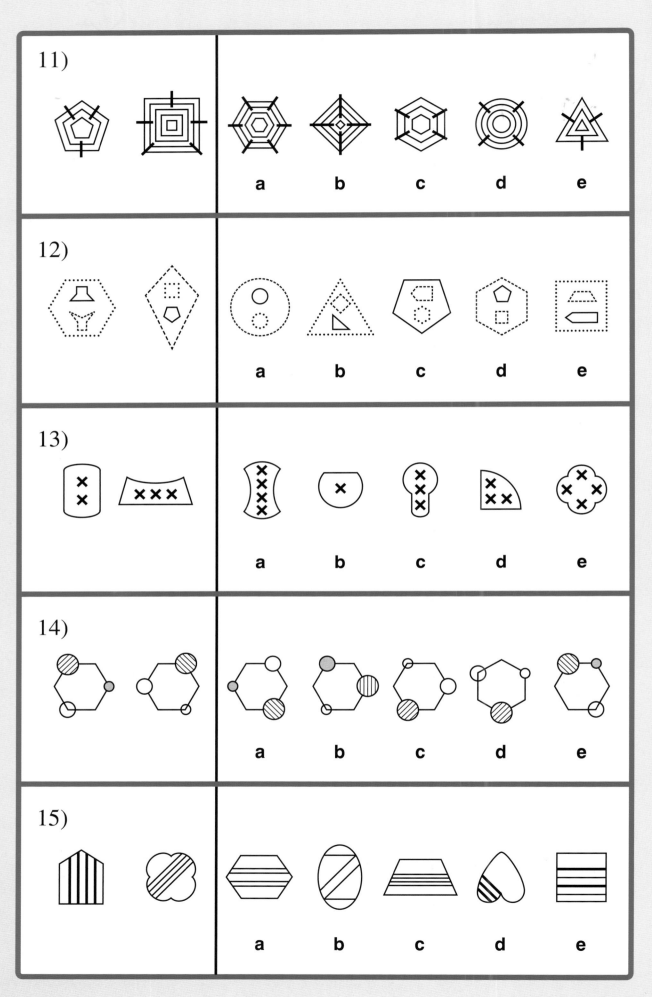

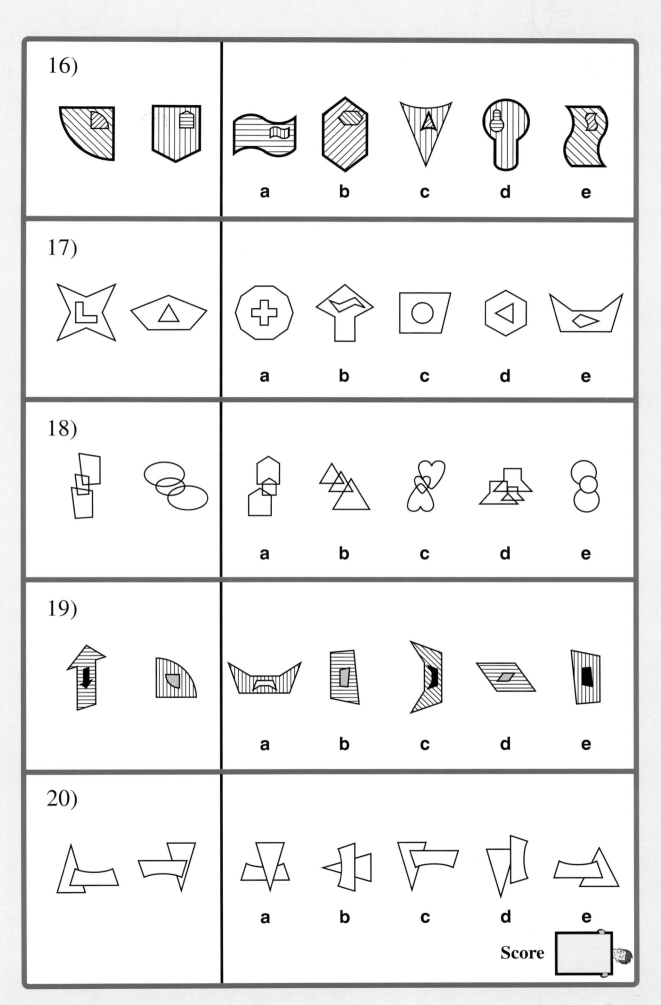

16)

          a   b   c   d   e

17)

          a   b   c   d   e

18)

          a   b   c   d   e

19)

          a   b   c   d   e

20)

          a   b   c   d   e

Score

Chapter Twenty-one
SERIES
1. Level One

To the left of each of the lines below there are five squares arranged in order. One of these squares has been left empty. Find which one of the five squares on the right should take the place of the empty square.

Example

	▫	◻	◻	

◻	◻	◻	◻	▫
a	**(b)**	c	d	e

Answer: **b** as the shape is enclosed by one more shape of the same type.

Exercise 21: 1 Which figure will complete the series?

1)

a   b   c   d   e

2)

a   b   c   d   e

3)

a   b   c   d   e

4)

a   b   c   d   e

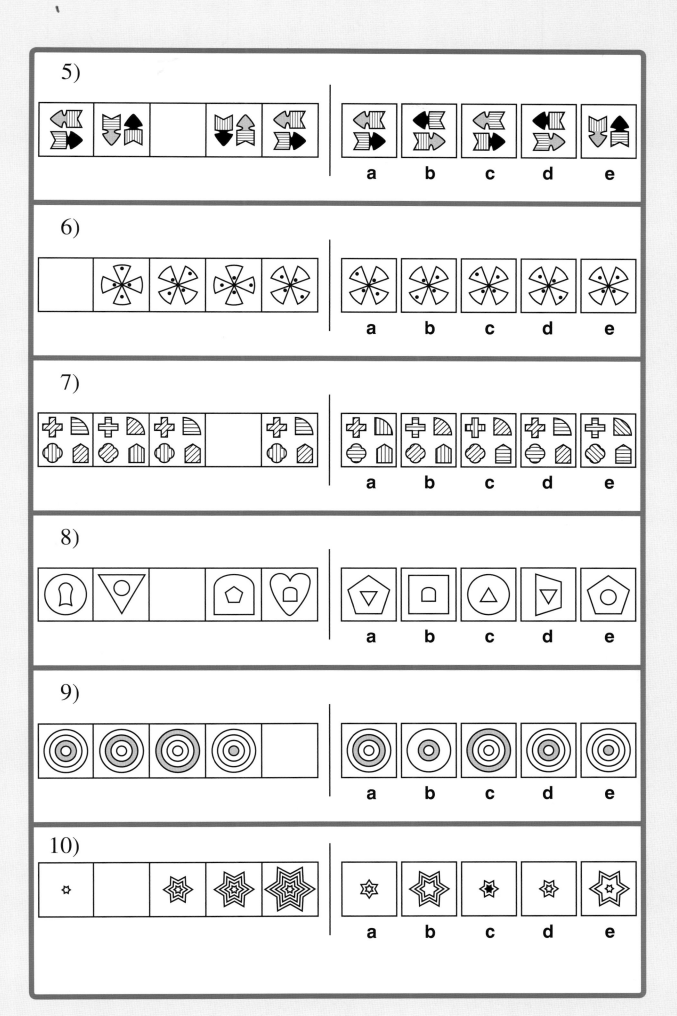

5)

6)

7)

8)

9)

10)

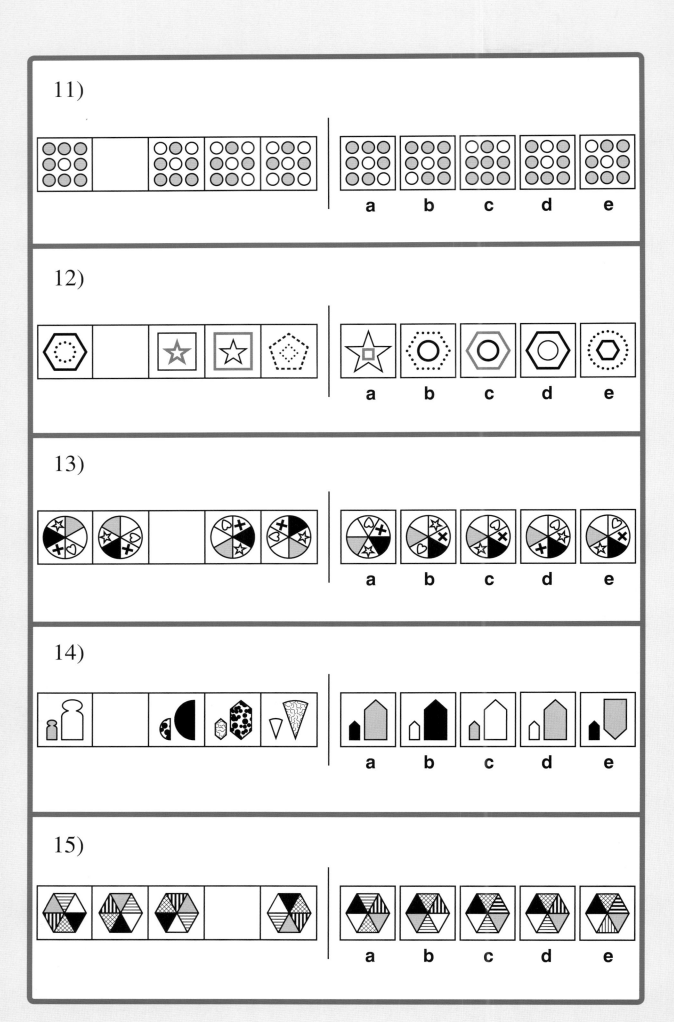

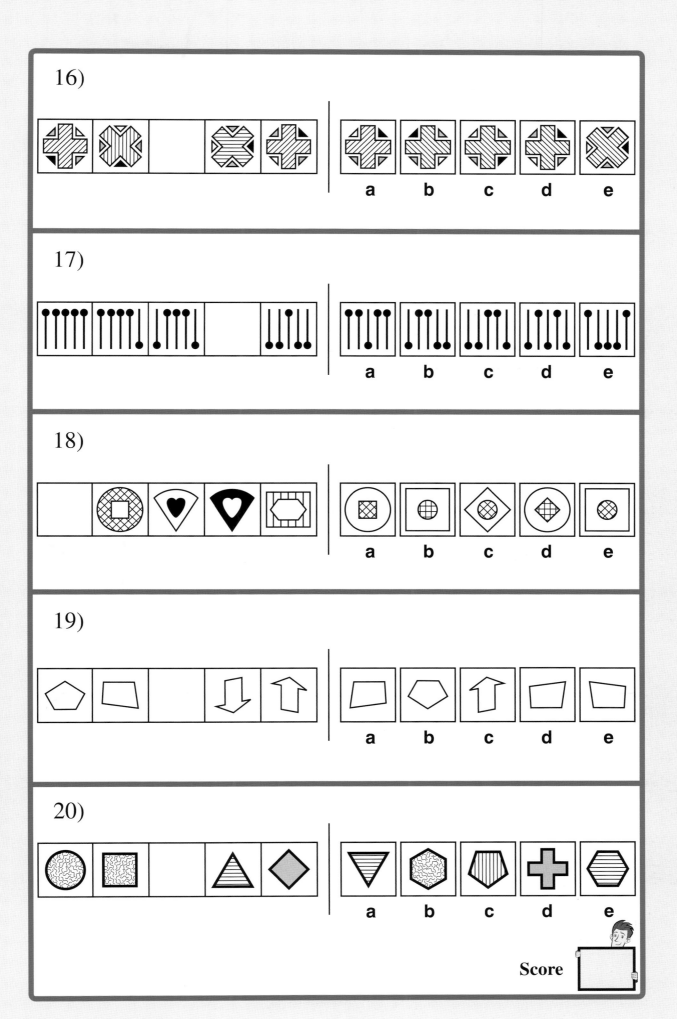

16)

17)

18)

19)

20)

Score

2. Level Two

To the left of each of the lines below there are five squares arranged in order. One of these squares has been left empty. Find which one of the five squares on the right should take the place of the empty square.

Example

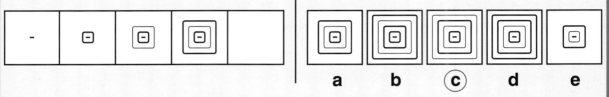

Answer: **c** as the shape is enclosed by one more shape of the same type and the solid lines alternate between Thin and Thick.

Exercise 21: 2 Which figure will complete the series?

1)

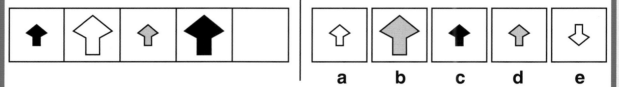

2)

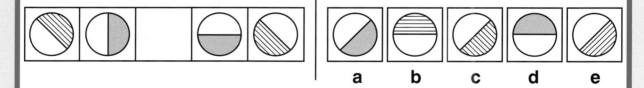

3)

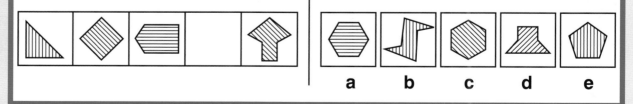

4)

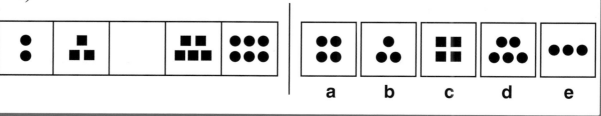

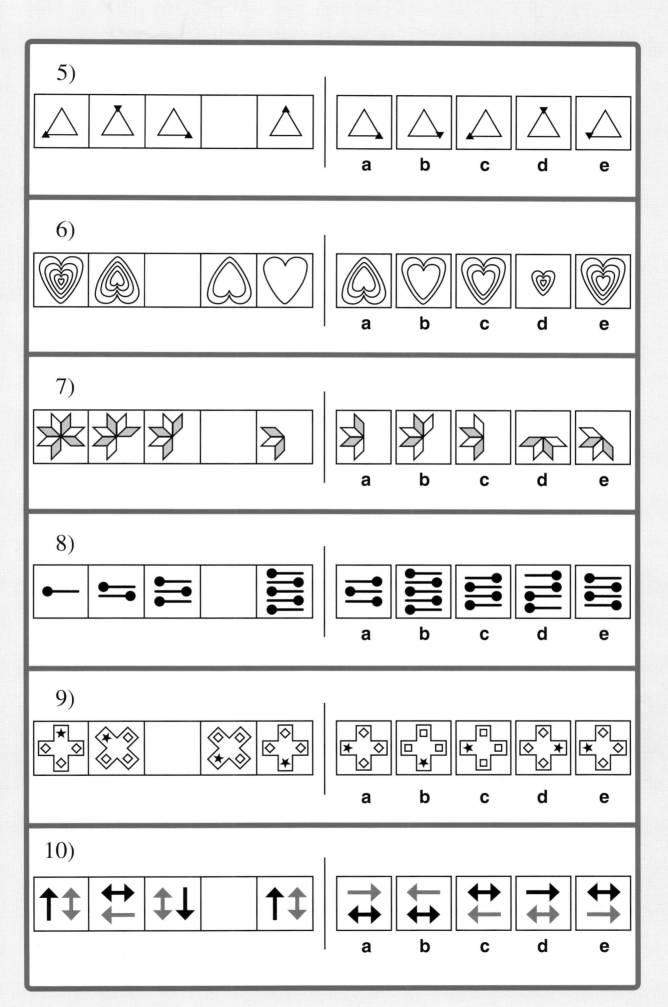

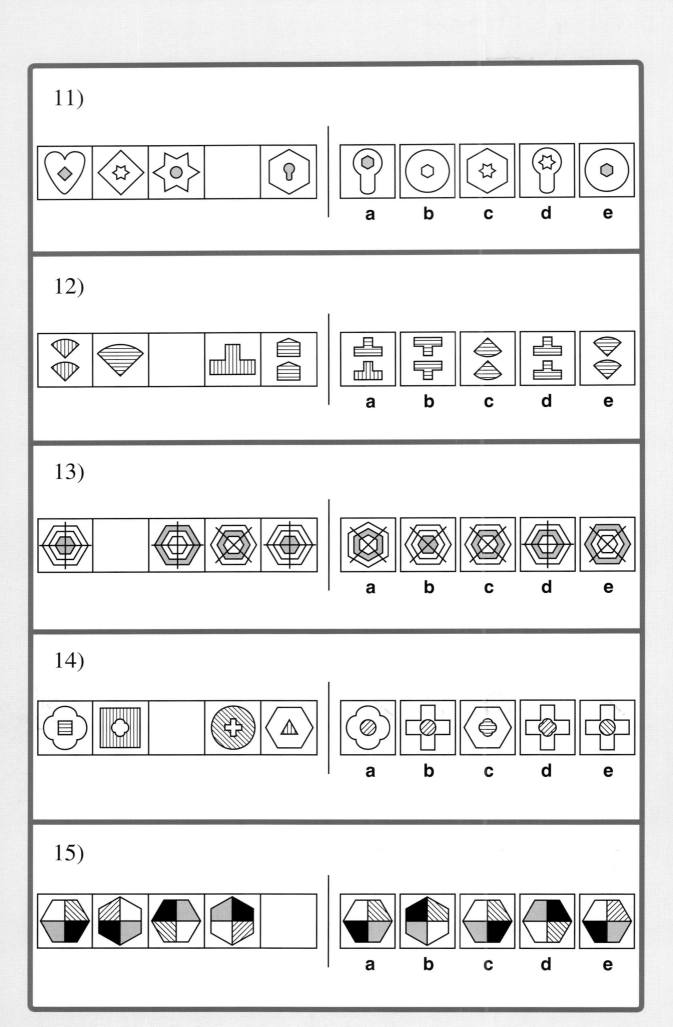

11)

12)

13)

14)

15)

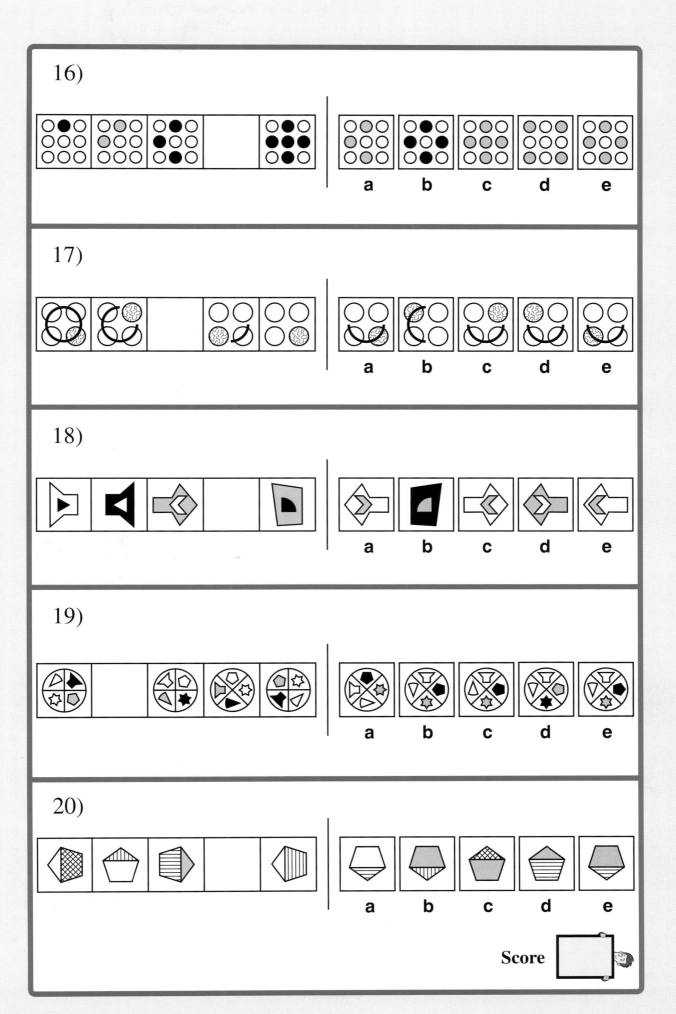

16)

17)

18)

19)

20)

Score

3. Level Three

To the left of each of the lines below there are five squares arranged in order. One of these squares has been left empty. Find which one of the five squares on the right should take the place of the empty square.

Example

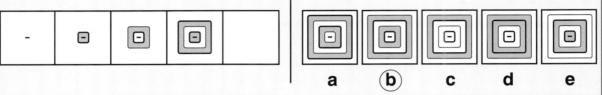

Answer: **b** as the shape is enclosed by one more shape of the same type, the solid lines alternate between Thin and Thick and the fills alternate between Grey and White from the outside towards the centre.

Exercise 21: 3 Which figure will complete the series?

1)

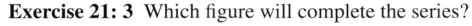

2)

3)

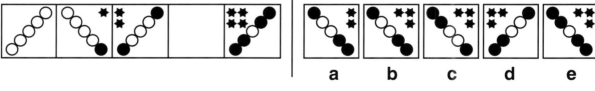

4)

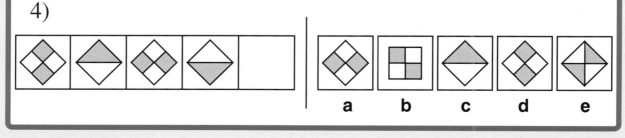

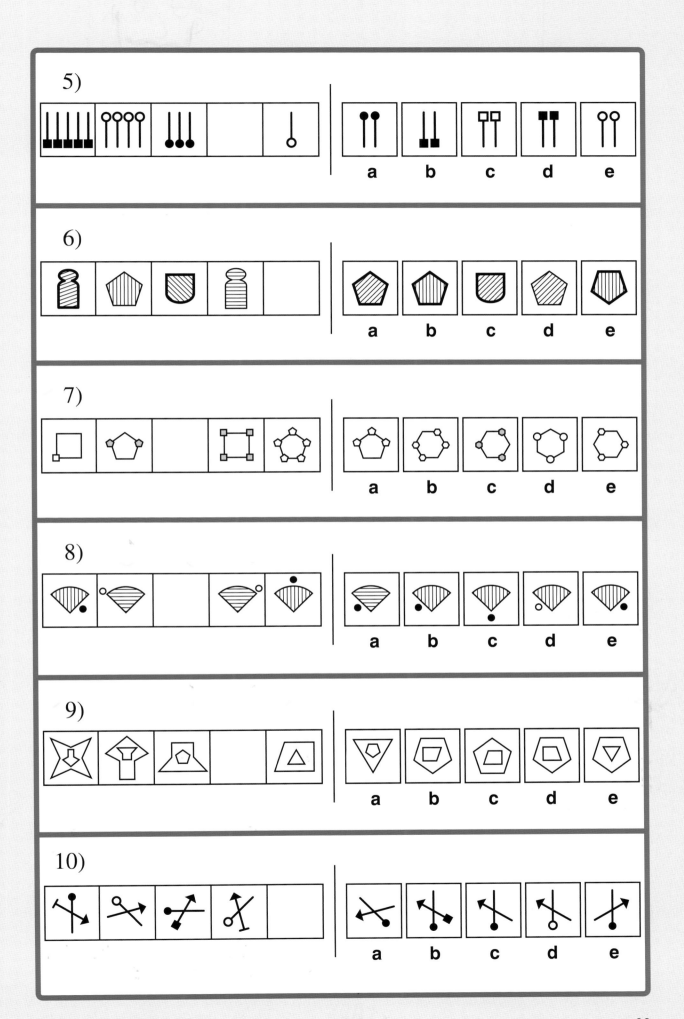

© 2011 Stephen Curran

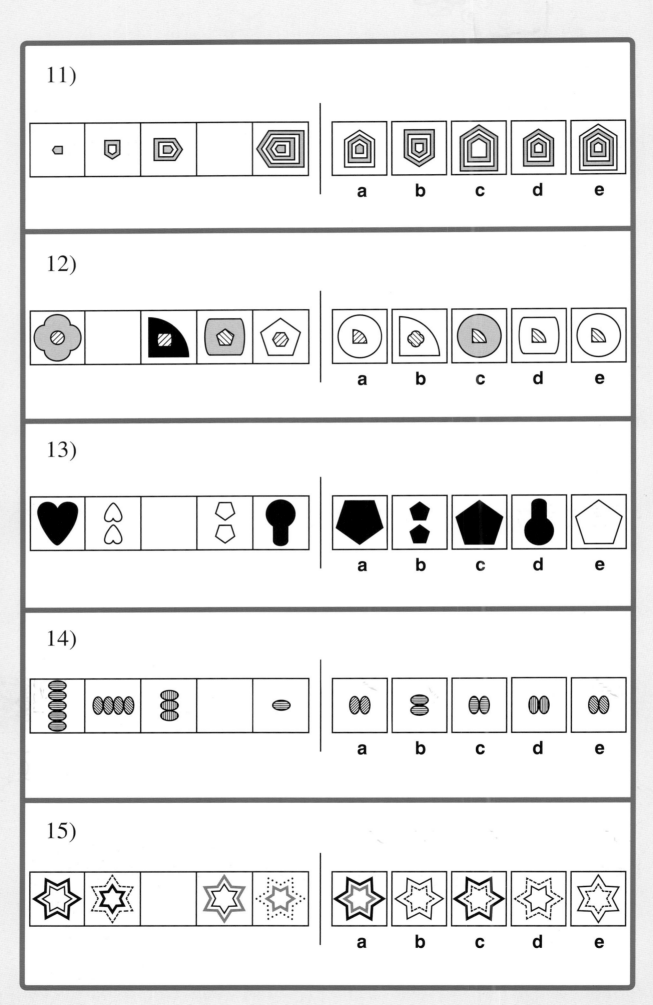

11)

a   b   c   d   e

12)

a   b   c   d   e

13)

a   b   c   d   e

14)

a   b   c   d   e

15)

a   b   c   d   e

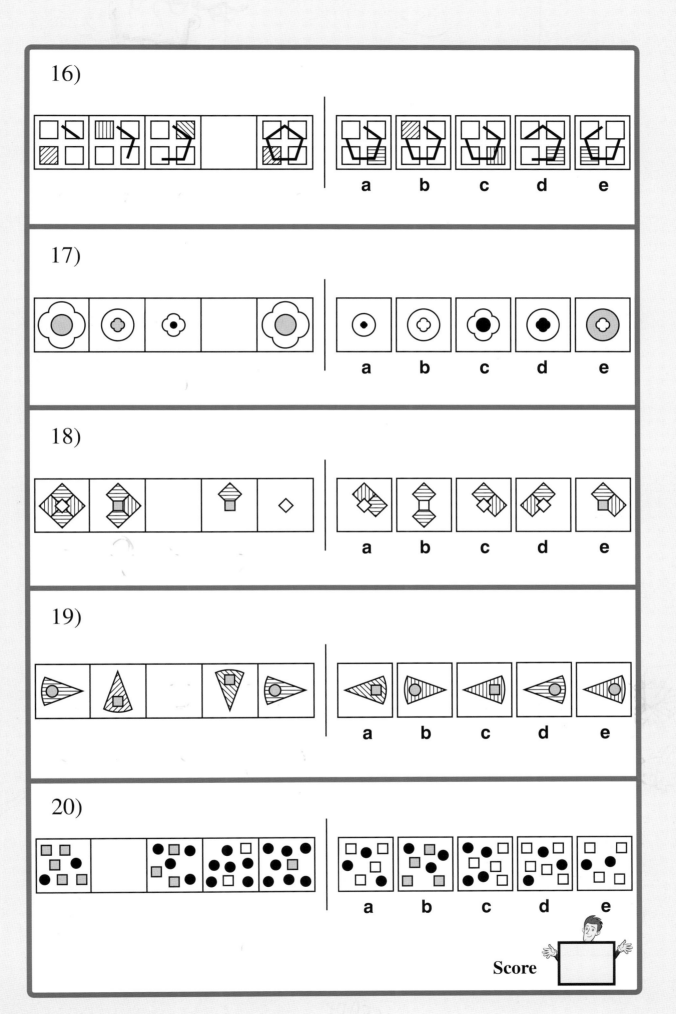

4. Levels Four & Five

To the left of each of the lines below there are five squares arranged in order. One of these squares has been left empty. Find which one of the five squares on the right should take the place of the empty square.

Example

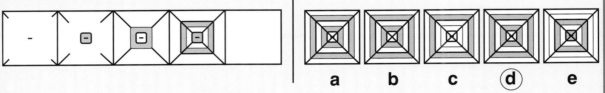

Answer: **d** as the shape is enclosed by one more shape of the same type, the solid lines alternate between Thin and Thick and the fills alternate between Grey and White from the outside towards the centre. Lines lengthen at each stage to form a Cross Shape at the end of the series.

Exercise 21: 4 Which figure will complete the series?

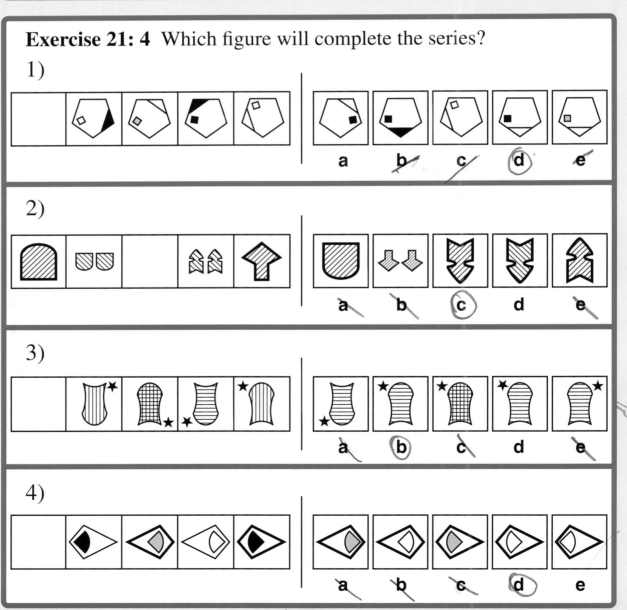

START

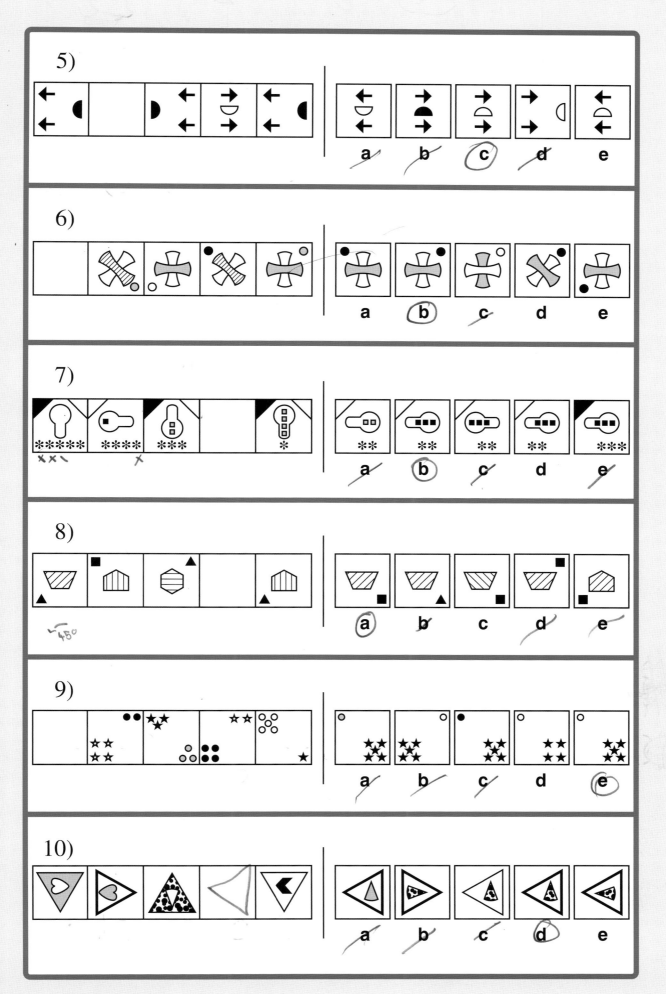

5)

a   b   c   d   e

6)

a   b   c   d   e

7)

a   b   c   d   e

8)

a   b   c   d   e

9)

a   b   c   d   e

10)

a   b   c   d   e

11)

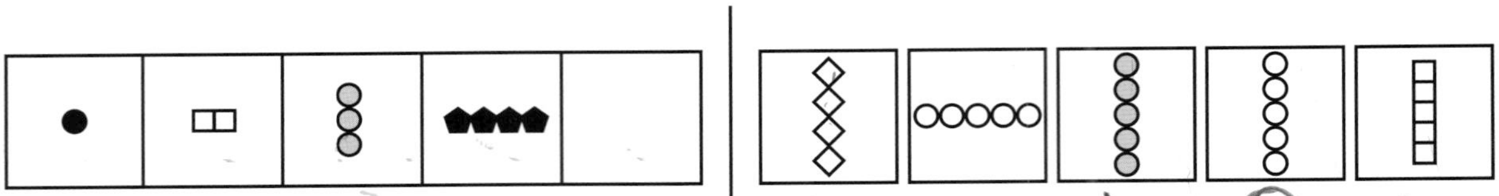

a   b   c   d   e

12)

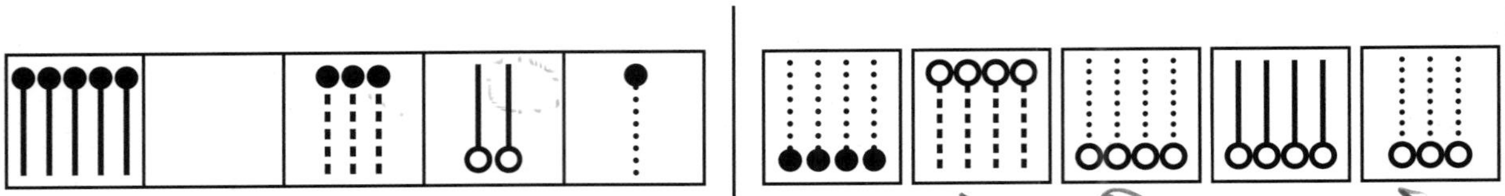

a   b   c   d   e

13)

a   b   c   d   e

14)

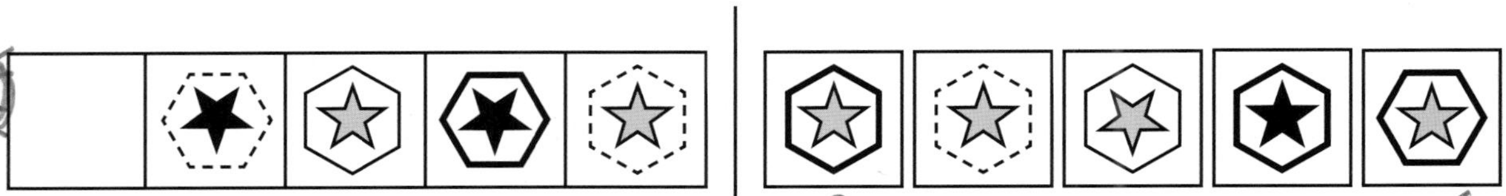

a   b   c   d   e

15)

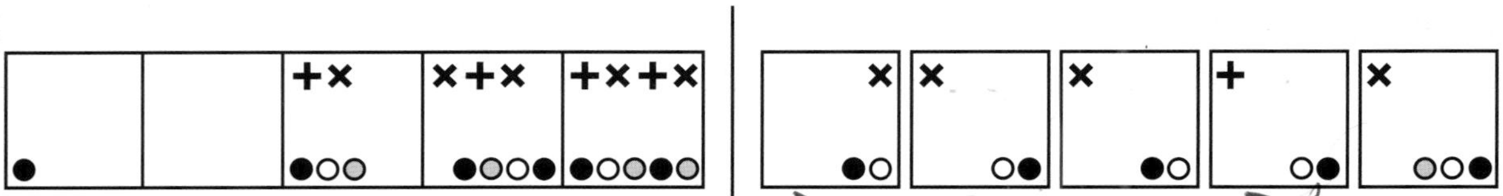

a   b   c   d   e

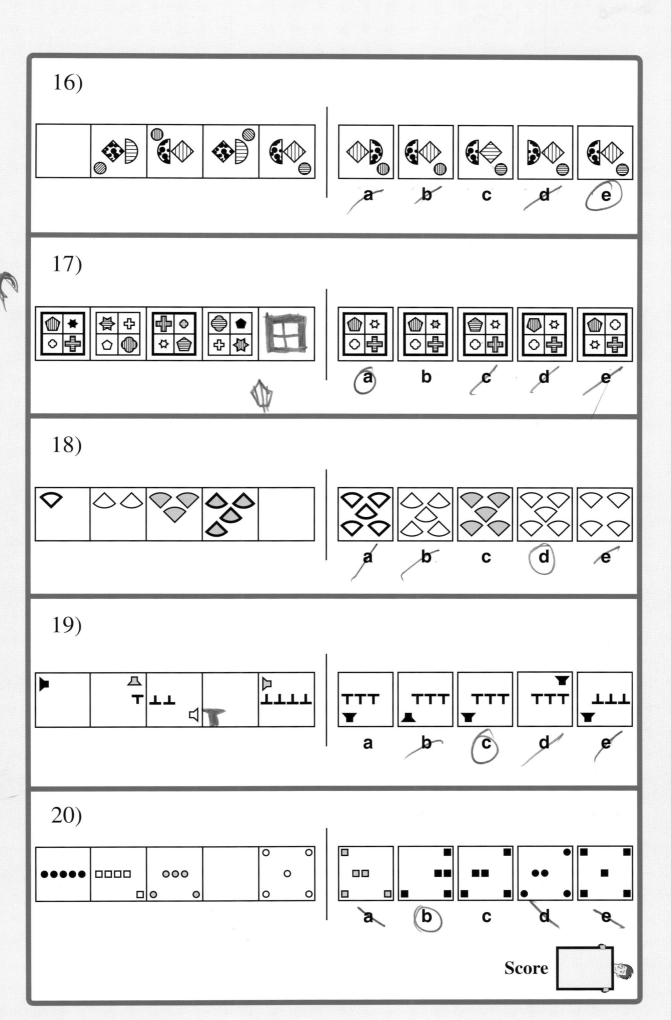

16)

a   b   c   d   **(e)**

17)

(a)   b   c   d   e

18)

a   b   c   **(d)**   e

19)

a   b   **(c)**   d   e

20)

a   **(b)**   c   d   e

Score

5. Mixed Levels

Exercise 21: 5 Which figure will complete the series?

1)

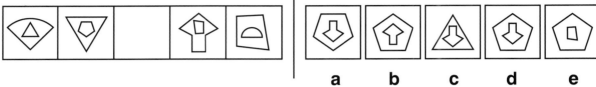

a b c d e

2)

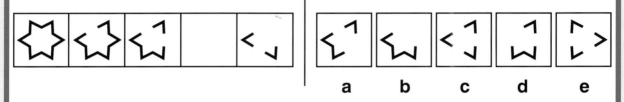

a b c d e

3)

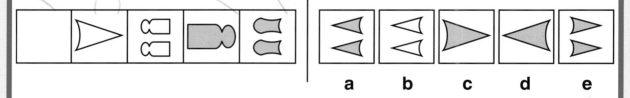

a b c d e

4)

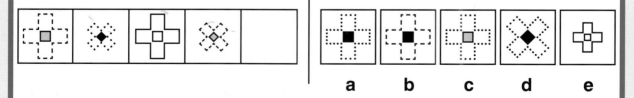

a b c d e

5)

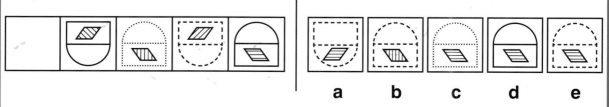

a b c d e

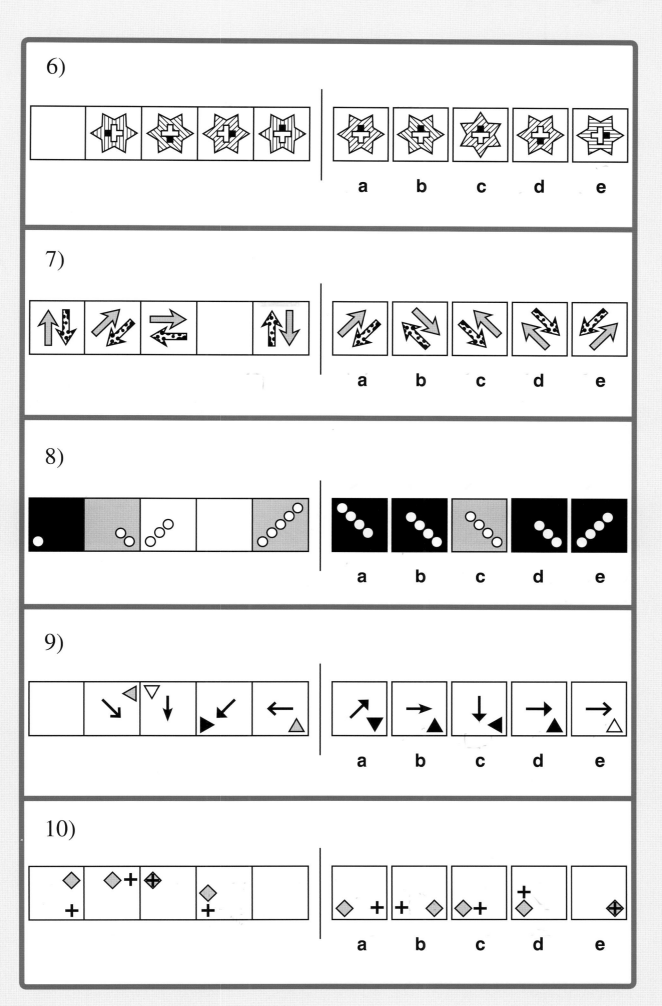

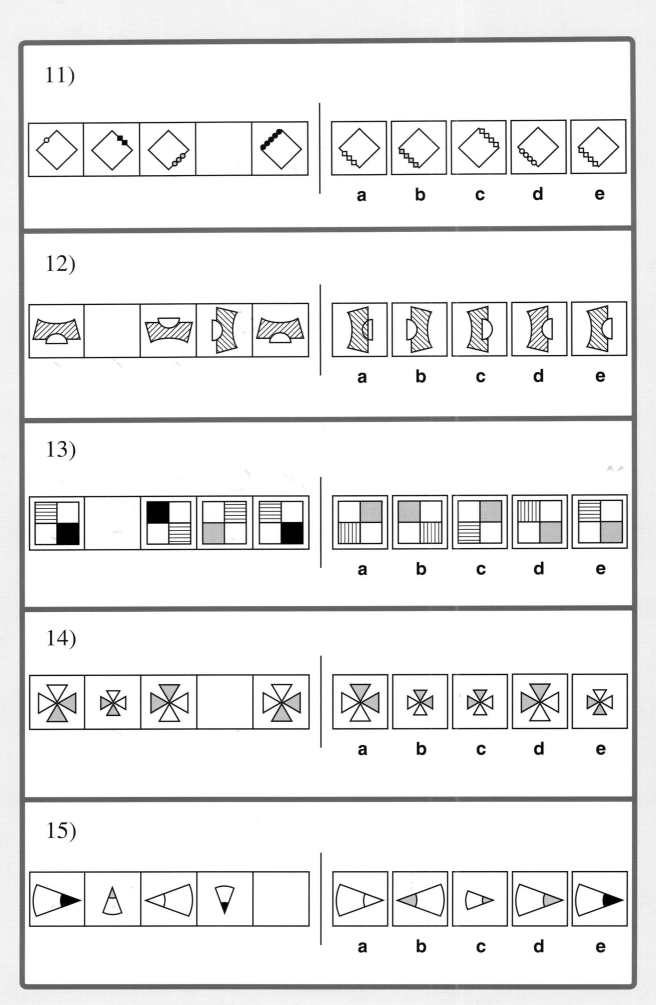

11)

a b c d e

12)

a b c d e

13)

a b c d e

14)

a b c d e

15)

a b c d e

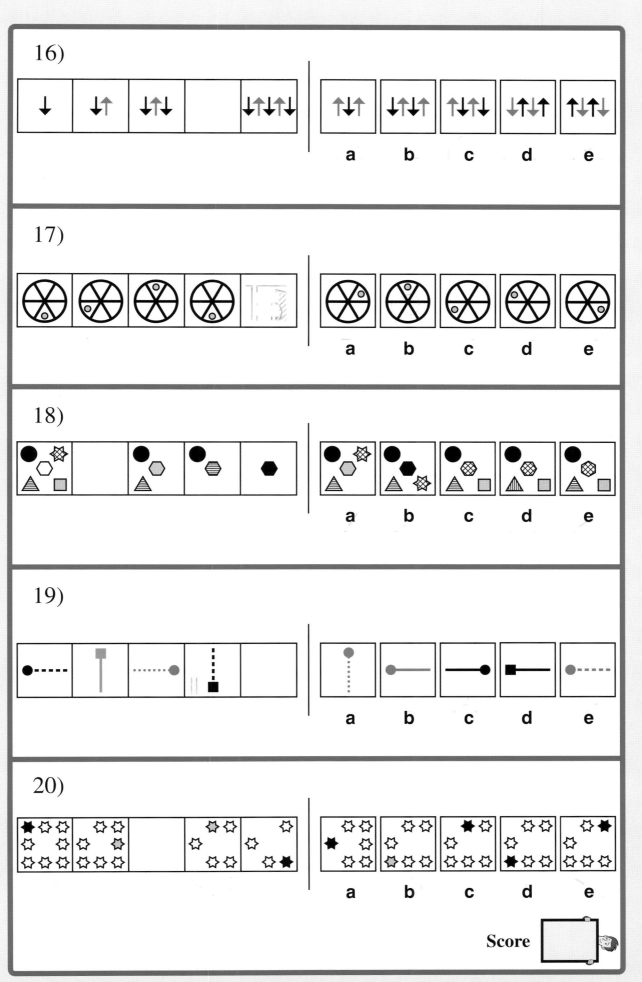

16)

17)

18)

19)

20)

Score

STOP

Chapter Twenty-two
MATRICES
1. Level One

In the big square on the left, one of the small squares has been left empty. One of the five figures on the right should fill the empty square. Find this figure.

Example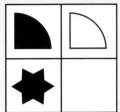

a   b   ⓒ   d   e

Answer: **c** as the fill has changed from Black to White horizontally.

Exercise 22: 1 Which figure should fill the empty square?

1)

a   b   c   d   e

2)

a   b   c   d   e

3)

a   b   c   d   e

4)

a   b   c   d   e

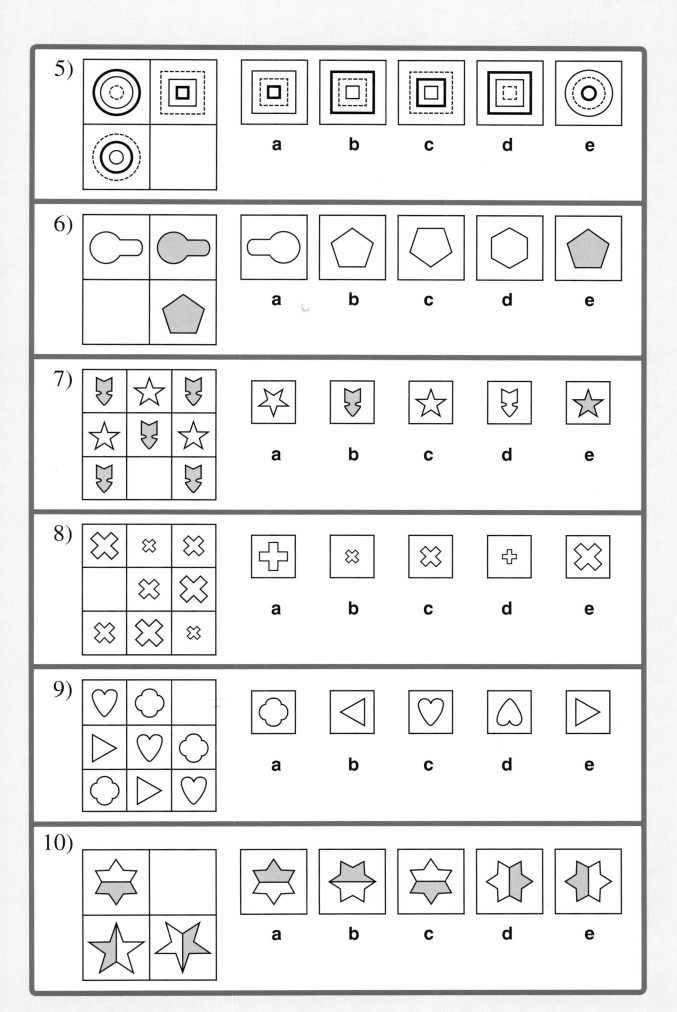

5)

a b c d e

6)

a b c d e

7)

a b c d e

8)

a b c d e

9)

a b c d e

10)

a b c d e

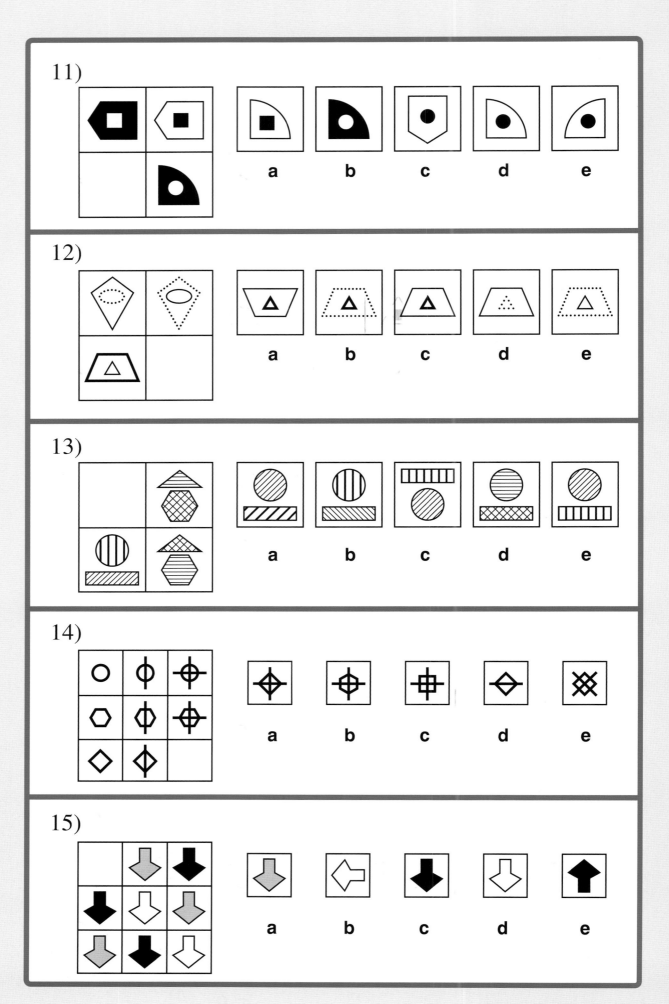

11)

a b c d e

12)

a b c d e

13)

a b c d e

14)

a b c d e

15)

a b c d e

16)

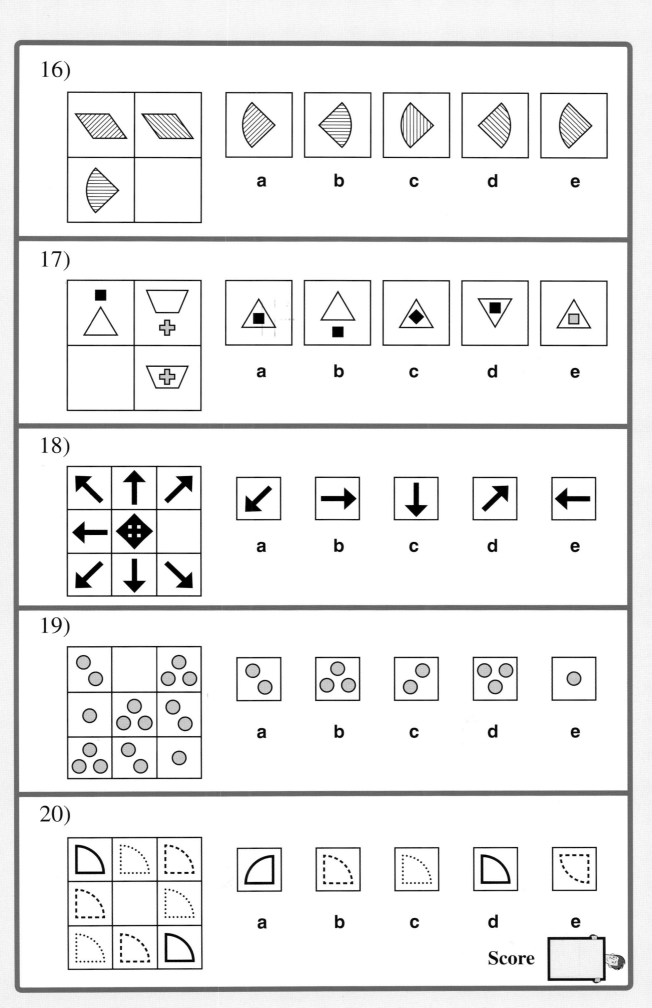

a   b   c   d   e

17)

a   b   c   d   e

18)

a   b   c   d   e

19)

a   b   c   d   e

20)

a   b   c   d   e

Score

2. Level Two

In the big square on the left, one of the small squares has been left empty. One of the five figures on the right should fill the empty square. Find this figure.

Example

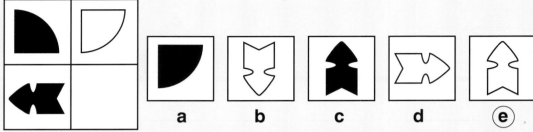

Answer: **e** as the fill has changed from Black to White and the shape has turned 90° in a clockwise direction horizontally.

Exercise 22: 2 Which figure should fill the empty square?

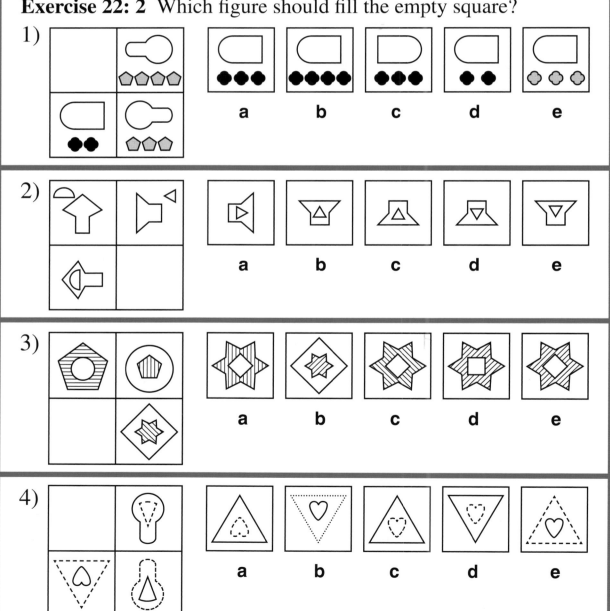

© 2011 Stephen Curran

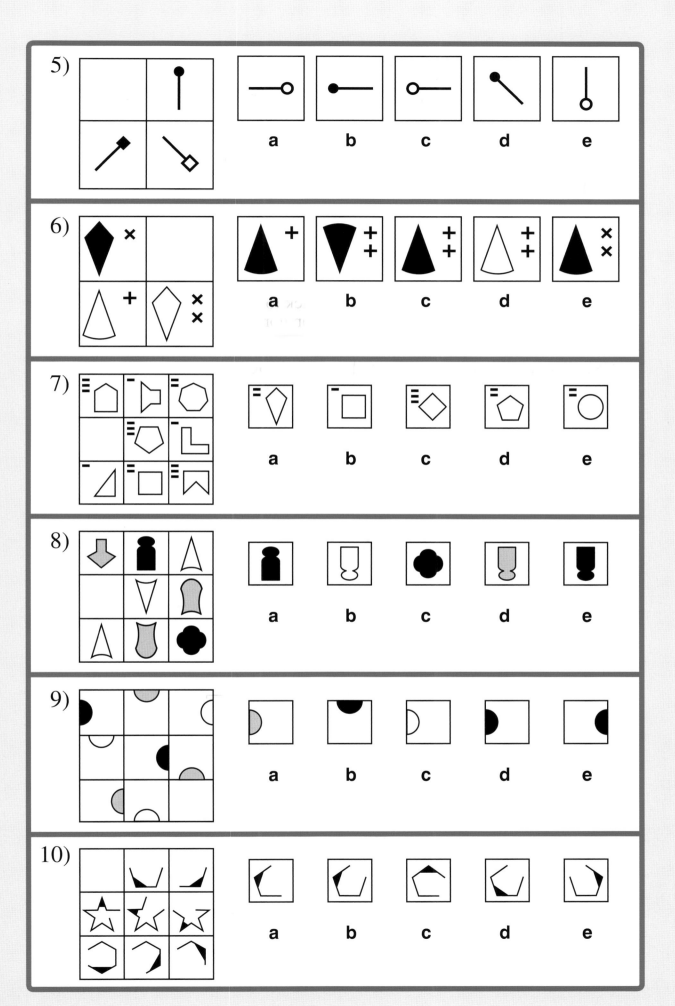

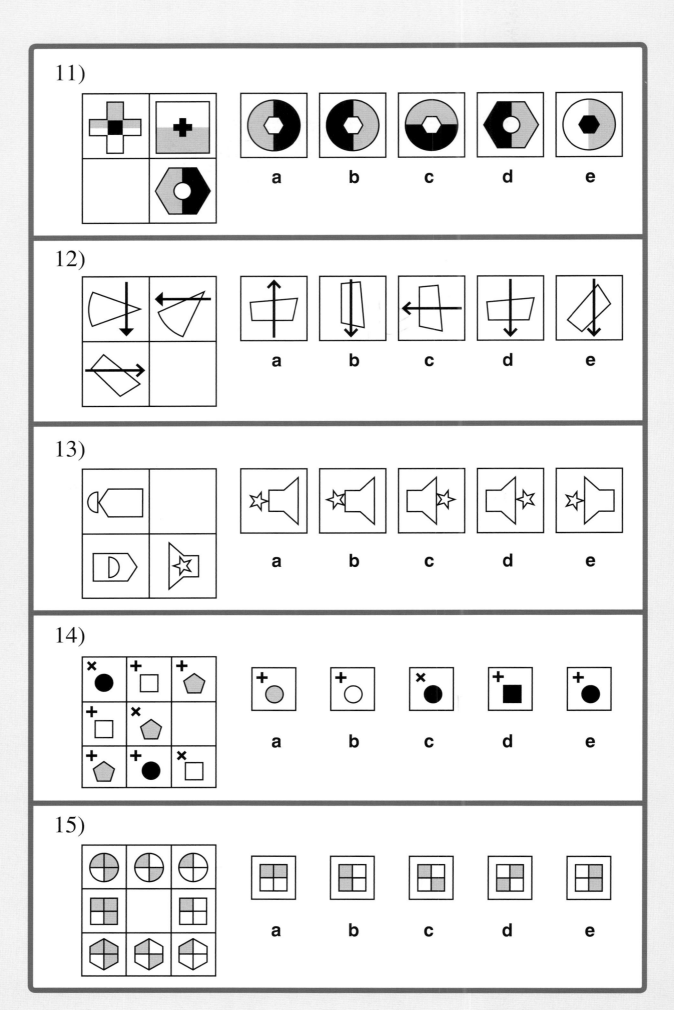

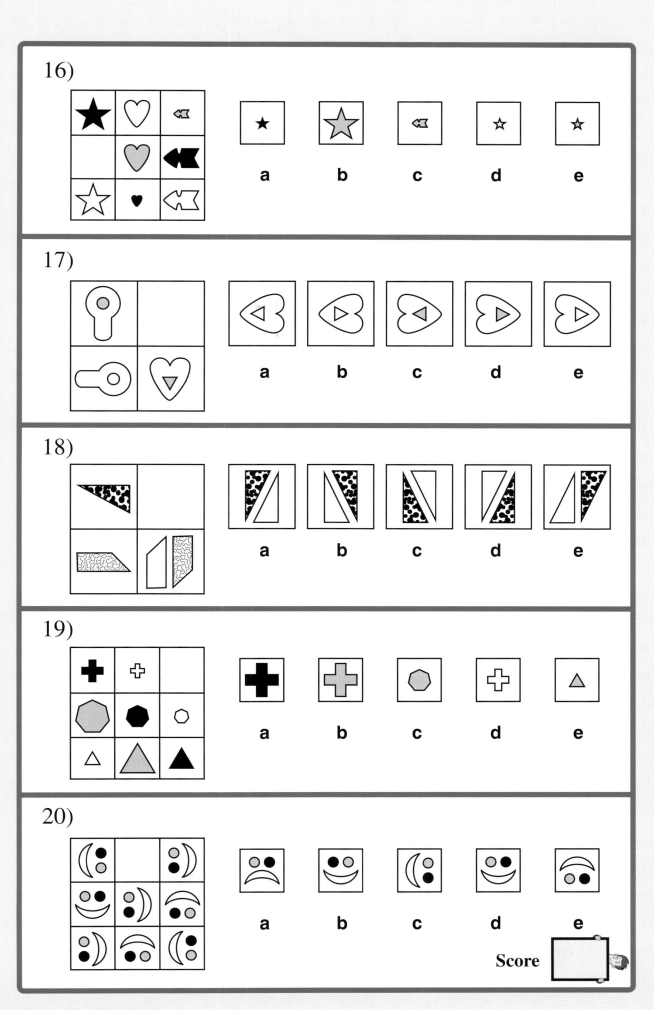

16)

a   b   c   d   e

17)

a   b   c   d   e

18)

a   b   c   d   e

19)

a   b   c   d   e

20)

a   b   c   d   e

Score

3. Level Three

In the big square on the left, one of the small squares has been left empty. One of the five figures on the right should fill the empty square. Find this figure.

Example

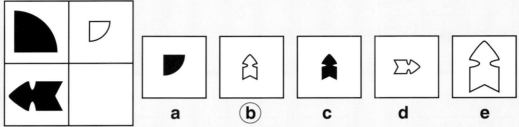

Answer: **b** as the fill has changed from Black to White, the shape has turned 90° in a clockwise direction and has reduced in size.

Exercise 22: 3 Which figure should fill the empty square?

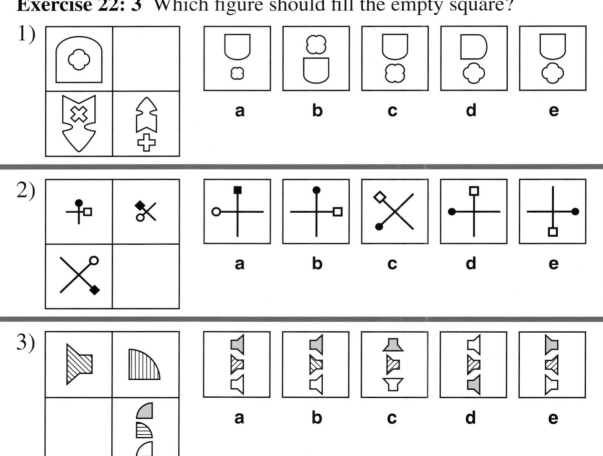

© 2011 Stephen Curran

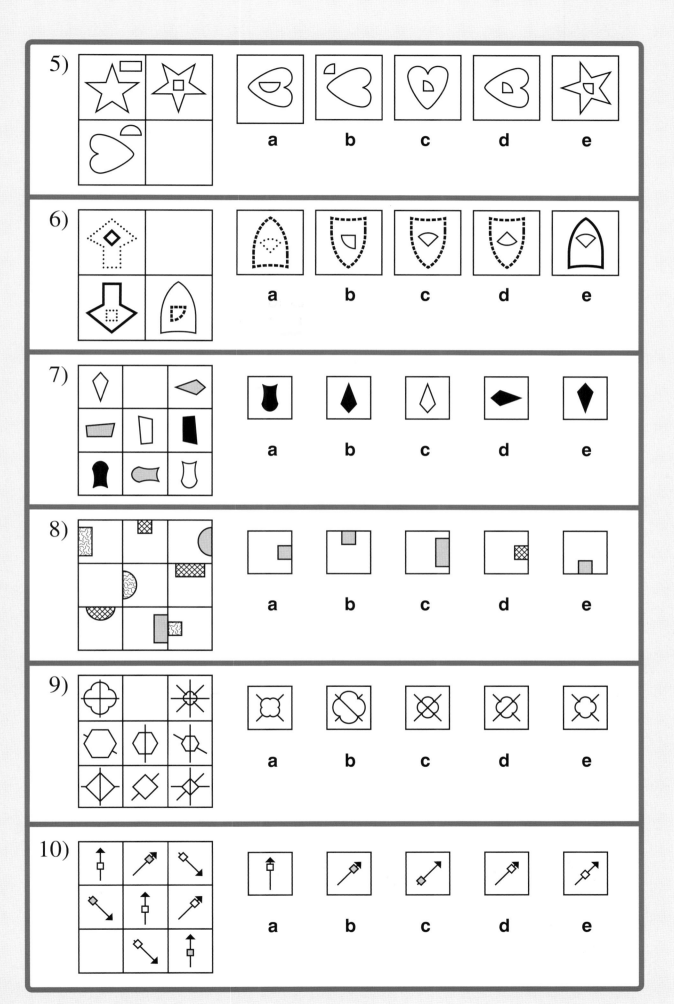

5)   a   b   c   d   e

6)   a   b   c   d   e

7)   a   b   c   d   e

8)   a   b   c   d   e

9)   a   b   c   d   e

10)   a   b   c   d   e

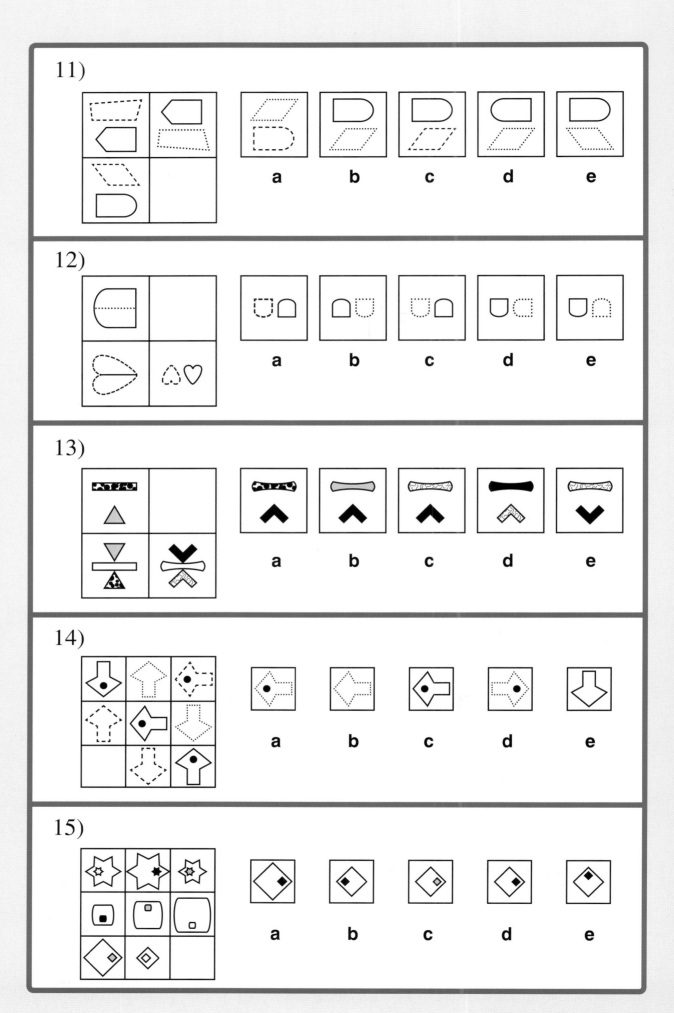

11)

a b c d e

12)

a b c d e

13)

a b c d e

14)

a b c d e

15)

a b c d e

54

© 2011 Stephen Curran

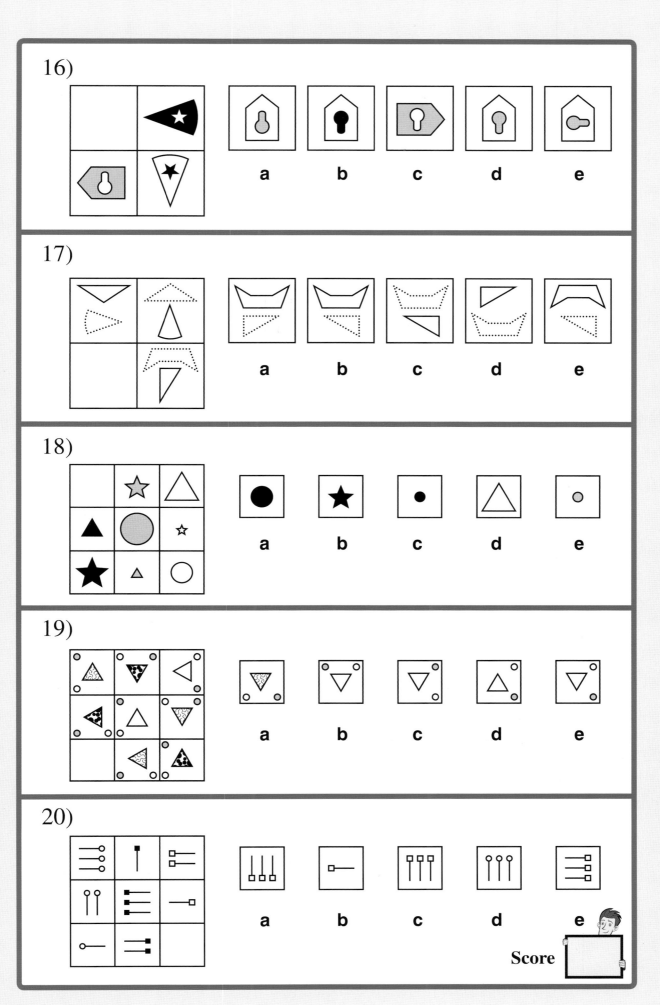

4. Levels Four & Five

In the big square on the left, one of the small squares has been left empty. One of the five figures on the right should fill the empty square. Find this figure.

Example

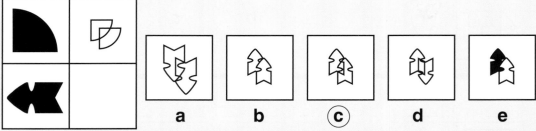

a   **b**   **ⓒ**   **d**   **e**

Answer: **c** as the fill has changed from Black to White and the shape has been turned 90° in a clockwise direction. An identical shape has been linked and both shapes have been reduced in size.

Exercise 22: 4 Which figure should fill the empty square?

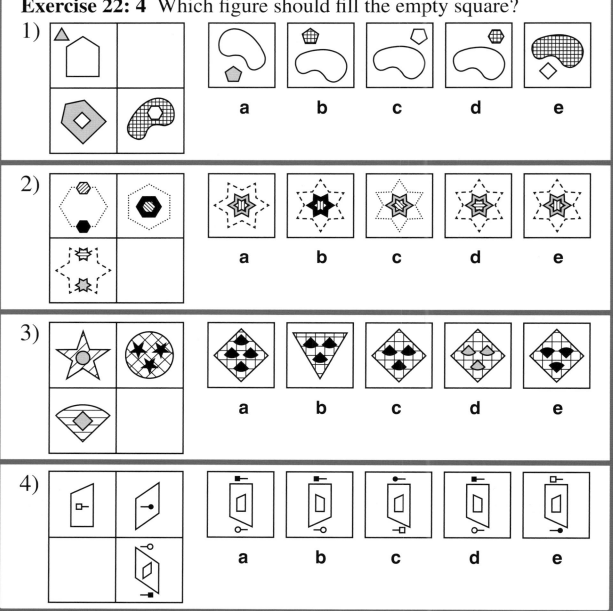

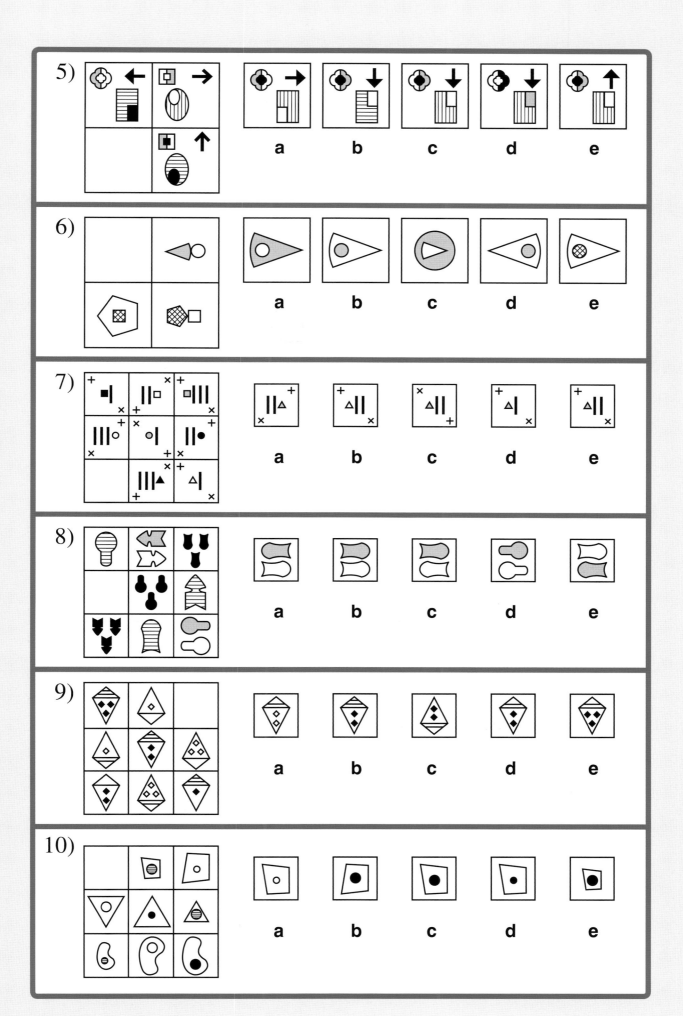

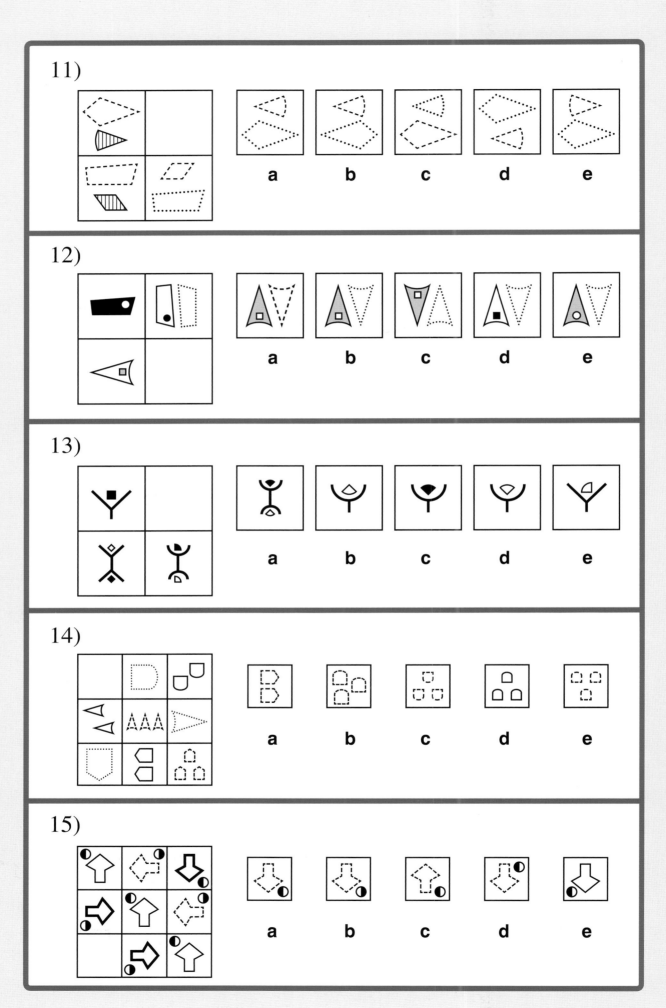

11)

a   b   c   d   e

12)

a   b   c   d   e

13)

a   b   c   d   e

14)

a   b   c   d   e

15)

a   b   c   d   e

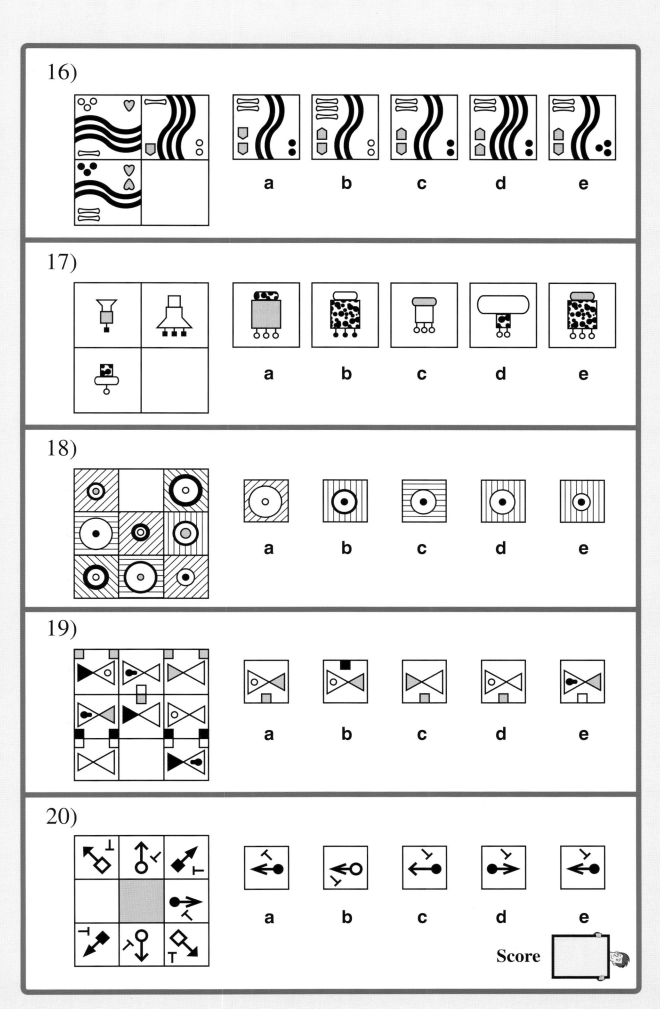

16)

a   b   c   d   e

17)

a   b   c   d   e

18)

a   b   c   d   e

19)

a   b   c   d   e

20)

a   b   c   d   e

Score

5. Mixed Levels

Exercise 22: 5 Which figure should fill the empty square?

1)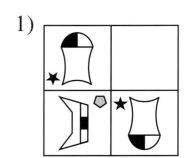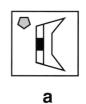

a   **b**   **c**   **d**   **e**

2)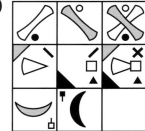

a   **b**   **c**   **d**   **e**

3)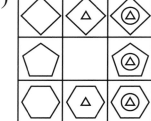

a   **b**   **c**   **d**   **e**

4)

a   **b**   **c**   **d**   **e**

5)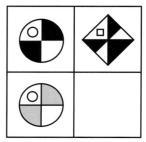

a   **b**   **c**   **d**   **e**

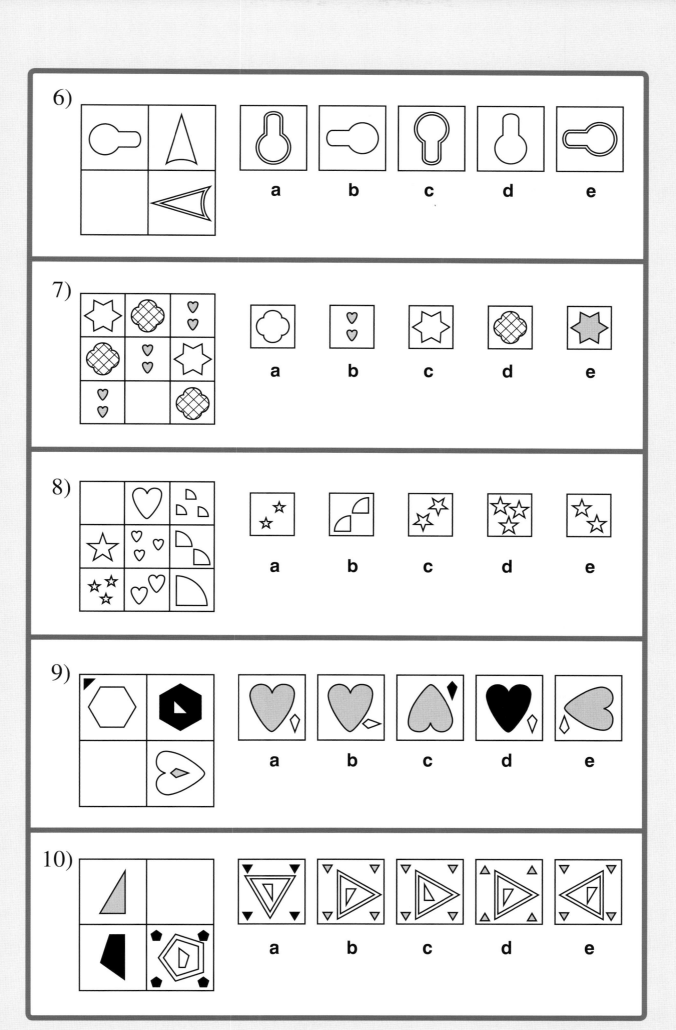

6)

7)

8)

9)

10)

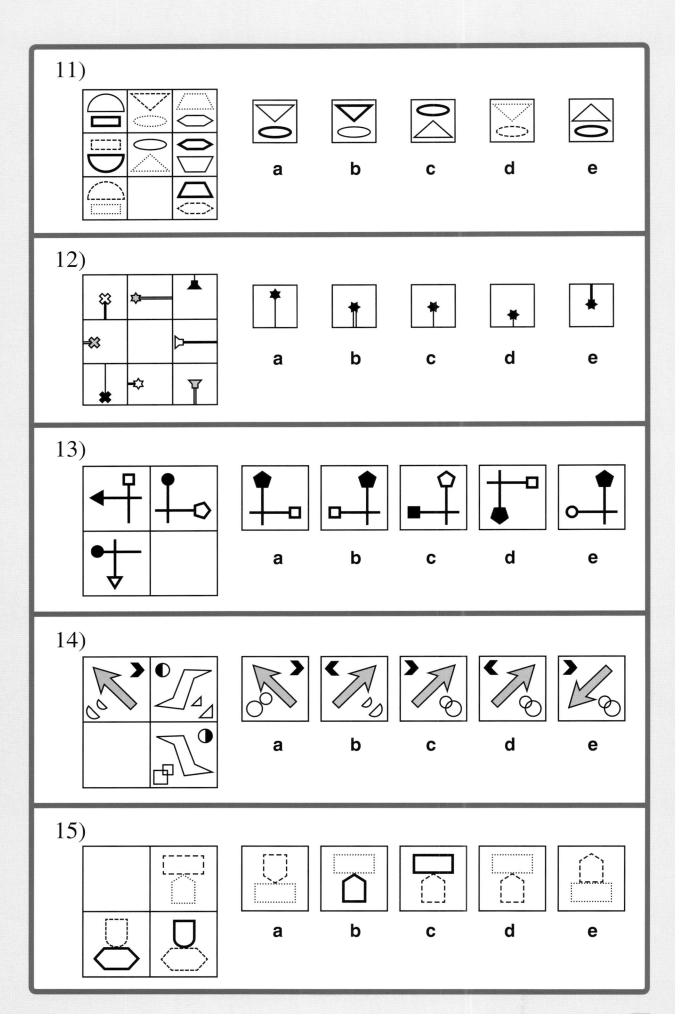

11)

a   b   c   d   e

12)

a   b   c   d   e

13)

a   b   c   d   e

14)

a   b   c   d   e

15)

a   b   c   d   e

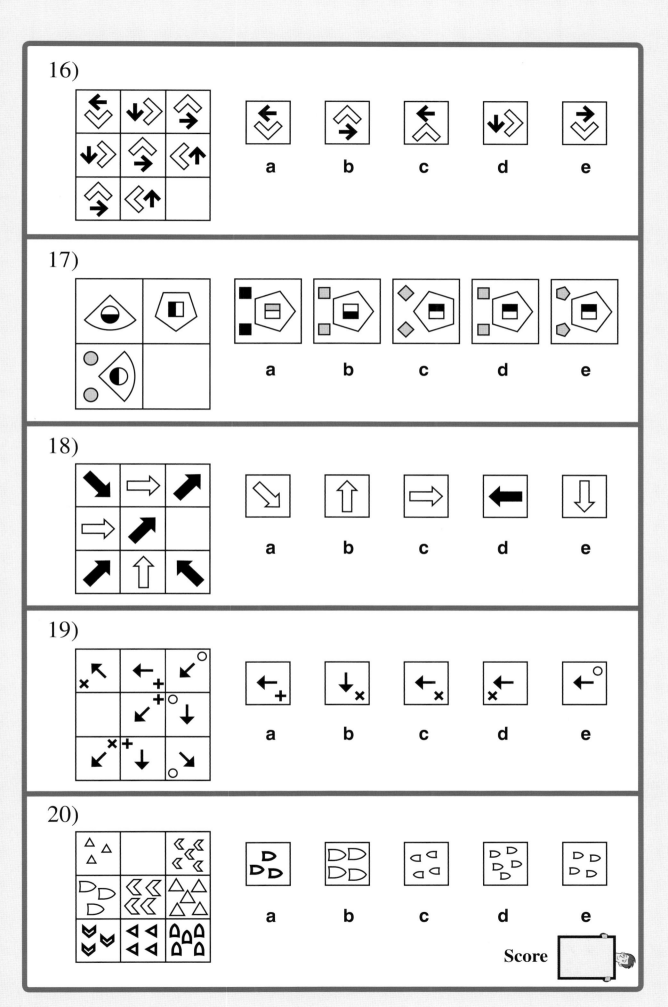

16)

a b c d e

17)

a b c d e

18)

a b c d e

19)

a b c d e

20)

a b c d e

Score

Answers

11+ Non-verbal Reasoning Year 5-7 Workbook 5

Chapter Twenty
Similarities
Exercise 20: 1
1) b
2) b
3) a
4) d
5) a
6) e
7) b
8) c
9) a
10) c
11) b
12) e
13) a
14) c
15) b
16) e
17) e
18) b
19) c
20) d

Exercise 20: 2
1) d
2) a
3) b
4) c
5) b
6) a
7) e
8) e
9) a
10) c
11) d
12) b
13) a
14) e
15) c
16) e
17) d

18) a
19) e
20) c

Exercise 20: 3
1) c
2) e
3) a
4) c
5) b
6) d
7) b
8) e
9) b
10) a
11) e
12) b
13) a
14) d
15) c
16) a
17) e
18) e
19) c
20) e

Exercise 20: 4
1) c
2) c
3) a
4) c
5) d
6) b
7) e
8) c
9) a
10) d
11) c
12) b
13) a
14) d
15) e
16) a

17) b
18) e
19) d
20) c

Exercise 20: 5
1) d
2) d
3) a
4) d
5) c
6) e
7) b
8) c
9) b
10) a
11) d
12) e
13) b
14) c
15) c
16) a
17) e
18) a
19) e
20) c

Chapter Twenty-one
Series
Exercise 21: 1
1) e
2) a
3) d
4) d
5) b
6) a
7) b
8) a
9) d
10) d
11) e
12) b

13) c
14) a
15) d
16) c
17) b
18) a
19) d
20) e

Exercise 21: 2
1) a
2) e
3) b
4) a
5) e
6) c
7) a
8) e
9) e
10) a
11) b
12) d
13) c
14) b
15) c
16) e
17) d
18) a
19) b
20) e

Exercise 21: 3
1) c
2) b
3) c
4) d
5) d
6) a
7) e
8) b
9) b
10) c
11) d

© 2011 Stephen Curran

65

Answers

12) **e**
13) **c**
14) **a**
15) **b**
16) **a**
17) **d**
18) **c**
19) **e**
20) **a**

Exercise 21: 4
1) **d**
2) **c**
3) **b**
4) **d**
5) **c**
6) **b**
7) **b**
8) **a**
9) **e**
10) **d**
11) **d**
12) **c**
13) **d**
14) **a**
15) **b**
16) **e**
17) **a**
18) **d**
19) **c**
20) **c**

Exercise 21: 5
1) **d**
2) **c**
3) **a**
4) **a**
5) **e**
6) **a**
7) **b**
8) **b**
9) **d**

10) **a**
11) **e**
12) **e**
13) **c**
14) **b**
15) **d**
16) **b**
17) **a**
18) **c**
19) **b**
20) **d**

Chapter Twenty-two
Matrices
Exercise 22: 1
1) **b**
2) **a**
3) **c**
4) **d**
5) **b**
6) **b**
7) **c**
8) **b**
9) **e**
10) **a**
11) **d**
12) **c**
13) **e**
14) **a**
15) **d**
16) **c**
17) **a**
18) **b**
19) **e**
20) **d**

Exercise 22: 2
1) **c**
2) **d**
3) **e**
4) **c**

5) **c**
6) **c**
7) **a**
8) **e**
9) **d**
10) **b**
11) **b**
12) **d**
13) **a**
14) **e**
15) **c**
16) **e**
17) **e**
18) **d**
19) **b**
20) **d**

Exercise 22: 3
1) **c**
2) **d**
3) **a**
4) **b**
5) **d**
6) **d**
7) **b**
8) **a**
9) **e**
10) **d**
11) **b**
12) **e**
13) **c**
14) **a**
15) **d**
16) **d**
17) **b**
18) **c**
19) **e**
20) **c**

Exercise 22: 4
1) **b**
2) **e**

3) **c**
4) **a**
5) **c**
6) **b**
7) **e**
8) **a**
9) **d**
10) **c**
11) **a**
12) **b**
13) **d**
14) **e**
15) **a**
16) **c**
17) **e**
18) **d**
19) **a**
20) **e**

Exercise 22: 5
1) **e**
2) **b**
3) **c**
4) **a**
5) **b**
6) **a**
7) **c**
8) **e**
9) **a**
10) **b**
11) **a**
12) **c**
13) **b**
14) **d**
15) **d**
16) **a**
17) **d**
18) **b**
19) **c**
20) **e**

PROGRESS CHART

Exercise	Mark	%
20: 1		
20: 2		
20: 3		
20: 4		
20: 5		
21: 1		
21: 2		
21: 3		
21: 4		
21: 5		
22: 1		
22: 2		
22: 3		
22: 4		
22: 5		

**Overall
Percentage**

%

CERTIFICATE OF

ACHIEVEMENT

This certifies

_____

has successfully completed

11+ Non-verbal Reasoning
Year 5–7
WORKBOOK **5**

Overall percentage
score achieved

%

Comment _____

_____

Signed _____

(teacher/parent/guardian)

Date _____